The Handbook of Pigeon Racing

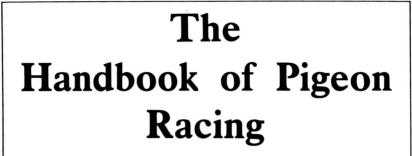

The Handbook of Pigeon Racing

JAN HERMANS

Translated by Robert R. Symonds

PELHAM BOOKS

First published in Great Britain by
Pelham Books Ltd
27 Wrights Lane
London W8 5TZ
1986

Originally published in the Netherlands and
Belgium as *Handboek Postduiven*
by Het Spectrum Publishing Co Ltd
Utrecht/Antwerp in collaboration with
Tros Television (Holland) and BRT (Belgium)

© Verbeek + Verbeek Boekprodukties bv,
's-Hertogenbosch 1986
English translation © Pelham Books 1986

British Library Cataloguing in Publication Data
Hermans, Jan
  The racing pigeon handbook.
  1. Homing pigeons
  I. Title   II. Handboek postduiven, *English*
  636.5'96   SF469
  ISBN 0 7207 1663 2

Set by Cambrian Typesetters, Frimley, Surrey, England
Printed in Belgium by Drukkerij Grafix Ltd, Retie

Contents

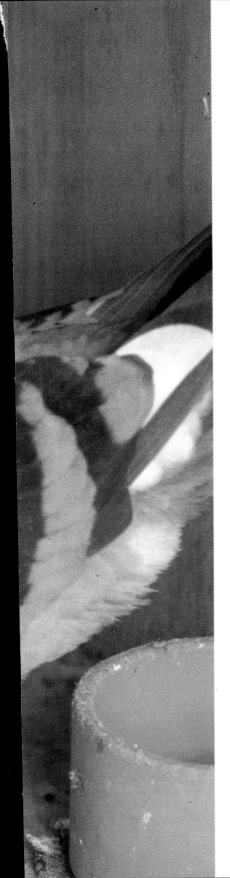

Foreword

In the summer of 1985 BRT (Belgium) and Tros
(Netherlands) television agreed to screen a co-
production about pigeon racing, a venture
supported by the Royal Belgian Pigeon Fanciers'
League (KBDB). It was the first time that serious
television coverage had been given to the sport and
that it had gained such a wide audience.

Many more people are now discovering the
fascination of the sport and why 150,000 fanciers
– grandfathers and grandsons, blue- and white-
collar workers alike – are so dedicated to pigeon
racing. With the help of many detailed illustrations, *The Handbook of Pigeon Racing* aims to
give as complete a picture of the hobby as possible.

Many people have helped in the production of
this book, enabling so many aspects, from breeding
to the actual racing and from housing to veterinary
care, to be dealt with exhaustively. My thanks to
them all. I should like though to make special
mention of Frans Hofmeester, my co-writer.
Without him the summer of 1985 would certainly
have been a less sunny one for me.

I hope this handbook will be a true guide to
many in the discovery of a new hobby. It has been
written for them.

Jan Hermans
August 1985

Foreword to the English edition

It gives me great pleasure to write the foreword to this excellent book. Pigeon racing is a most exciting sport. It involves the breeding, selection and conditioning of one of nature's smaller species and racing them against the clock over distances in excess of 500 miles. There is little to compare with the feeling of elation felt when a pigeon, specially bred and raced, appears as a dot in the sky and eventually folds its wings and drops into the loft.

This book, written by Jan Hermans, is one of the better books on pigeon racing. It is written to be of use to both beginner and experienced fancier alike and is also excellently illustrated. I wish the book every success.

Major E. C. Camilleri (Ret'd)
Royal Pigeon Racing Association
June 1986

Note to the reader

Jan Hermans gives a detailed description of the
breeding, management and conditioning of pigeons for
racing. He also gives an insight into the organization of
pigeon racing in Holland and Belgium. While some of
this is not applicable in detail to the United Kingdom, it
is none the less very interesting to see how racing is
organized and administered in those countries.

This book is a must for every pigeon fancier's library.

INTRODUCTION

Historical documents from all cultures refer to the relationship between man and the homing pigeon. The dove is depicted in carvings and decorative objects which have been preserved or dug up. The ancient Chinese, Greek and Roman literatures contain eulogies of the bird and associate it with innocence and love. But great writers from the more recent past – Shakespeare, Wordsworth, Dumas, Dickens – use the dove as a means of greater expressiveness:

Jan Hermans,
Mgr. Bannenberglaan 6,
5581 AH Waalre Holland
phone: 00-31.4904.15575

> '. . . Anon as patient as the female dove,
> When that her golden couplets are disclos'd,
> His silence will sit drooping.'
> (Shakespeare, Hamlet, Act V, Scene 1).

Religions regard the dove as a sacred bird. From distant antiquity and from Japan to Egypt, from India to Italy, they form part of everyday life in the farmyard and city dwelling. Pigeons are kept by no means only for their agreeable companionship, but also as a permanent source of meat supply and of manure for the fields.

It is known that these birds were also useful at sea. Fishermen in the countries around the Mediterranean Sea carried them in their boats. When they began the homeward voyage they released the pigeons to warn their fellow villagers to get everything ready for receiving the catch. Scenes of such 'releases' can be seen on ancient Egyptian monuments. Pigeons were also to be found at court. Monarchs and princes enjoy the company of these winged friends up to the present day.

As numerous other examples show, the pigeon has long appealed to the imagination and it still does so. Organizations of owners of homing or racing pigeons – to give but two of the most used names – are to be found in about forty countries. And then we are referring to but one member of the widely branching dove family. Although circumstances have changed and the hobby or sport has altered in character, the many hundreds of thousands of enthusiasts still exploit the same outstanding and thrilling qualities of this athlete which have brought man and bird so close to each other over the centuries.

Author Jan Hermans is not only
active in organisation and as a
publicist, he is as well a well-known
fancier and owner of a very valuable
collection topbirds. The strains in his
loft are mainly Tournier, Gebr.
Janssen and Aarden. His favorite bird
is without any doubt SMARAGD-
BARCELONA NL 82-1200025.
This marvelous hen, as strong as iron,
was bred and raced by Mr. Van
Leeuwen and was transfered to Jan
Hermans.
She is one of the best Barcelone-hens
all times.
Sire is a direct M. van Geel
(=Aarden) from Brother DOLLE and
dam is a crossing M. van Geel ×
Kuypers Brothers.
In 1984 she won in the Barcelona-
race (1175 km) 1st national and 1st
International against 2949 hens and in
1985 1st national and 2nd
International against 3254 hens.

There are many old engravings, some more detailed than others, of wild pigeons, rock doves and other relatives of the modern racing pigeon. Pictures such as that of 'The Milker' give an impression of our predecessors in the hobby. The photograph on the facing page shows a dovecot, the forerunner of the present-day loft. Today, however, the keeping of pigeons is no longer a 'manorial right' as under the old laws.

The oldest sources

Kamadeva, the god of love in one of the oldest and greatest religions in the world, Hinduism, was always depicted in the company of bees and doves. The Christian religions are familiar with the Old Testament story of Noah who released the dove from the ark three times after the Flood to see whether the surface of the earth was dry. (A similar legend also exists in other religions.) There is also reference at various places in the Bible to the use of a young pigeon or turtle dove, such as for the 'purification' of women after the birth of a child or for other sacrificial ceremonies. It is therefore not surprising that we read in Isaiah: 'Who are these that fly as a cloud, and as the doves to their windows?' The poor, in particular, were allowed to erect dovecots, so that they could bring their sacrifices to the Temple.

Very old records are also available from the Assyrians, Sumerians, Canaanites, Persians, Egyptians, Phoenicians and many other peoples, in which doves play a leading or subsidiary role. Terracotta images of these birds have been found dating from a period from 2,000 to 5,000 years BC. They show a surprising resemblance to the present-day racing pigeon. Many of the great Greek and Roman authors and historians mention doves: Homer, Aristotle, Virgil and Pliny, to name only some of the best known.

Messengers of disaster and love

The part which doves played and which is referred to in so many of the old stories always relates to their homing ability (see The Sport). It is this instinct which enables the birds to reach the nest or the loft from a distant and unknown destination. The role of the birds, based on this ability, was to carry messages.

Victories, but also defeats, of kings and generals were reported to the home front by this means. Nor did these gentlemen and certain Greek ladies hesitate to entrust amorous and, therefore, intimate outpourings to the dove's breast. The Greek poet Anachreon, for example, told of this practice in as early as 500 BC.

With some poetic licence these messages could be described as the forerunners of the rings which are fitted to the present-day homing pigeon. The modern foot rings incidentally speak a more sober language than the

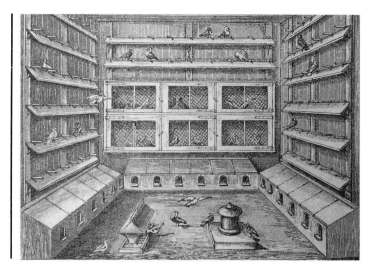

Historical documents in many languages pay much attention to the pigeon and its housing. The handsome specimens below were drawn by Jean Bungartz and were published in print in Leipzig at the end of the last century.

honeyed words of lovelorn kings! The ancient Egyptians even developed a distant predecessor of our modern airmail paper: small sheets measuring just six by nine centimetres and with a weight of 50 grammes per square metre.

Thus the word victory, or the opposite, has always played an important role in the communication function of the pigeon, as, for example, in the sports arena. The combined Olympic games of antiquity brought a veritable aerial fleet on the wing to carry the names of the winners to the most distant parts of the country. Aelianus set down a report in 230 AD about Taurosthenes, the first marathon runner, who was both a good sportsman and a skilled pigeon fancier. He took with him to the arena at Pisa a female pigeon which had chicks in the nest. After the victory he bound a piece of the winning tape around the neck of the bird which, following its instinct, quickly flew back to its nest. Taurosthenes' fellow villagers learned at the same time that their representative had placed the name of their village, Aeguina, on record for posterity. Apart from fighting, the Roman gladiators also knew about pigeons. They used them to report their victories and so ensure that their fees were increased for future appearances.

News reports
Later, in about the middle of the 12th century, pigeons provided a regular service between Baghdad, the capital of what is now Iraq, and the other great cities of what was then Syria. The Sultan ordered dovecots to be built in his realm and stocked with birds as a means of spreading the news of the day. We can learn in John Moore how Dutch seafarers imported the first homing pigeons from Baghdad. They were called 'Baghdads'

On the way to success, but disappointment lies close to victory.

after their place of origin. It can be assumed that the racing pigeons in the Low Countries are the descendants of these Persian imports.

The news of Napoleon's defeat at Waterloo was carried by Nathan Rothschild's fast fliers. The banking house he founded partly owes its wealth to the speed at which use could be made of this report on the London Stock Exchange. The potential of the pigeon for the rapid transmission of price quotations was also appreciated on other stock exchanges. At the beginning of the last century services were organised between Paris, Amsterdam, London and Frankfurt. There was also a regular link between Antwerp and London.

In the last century Dutch and Belgian newspapers depended on homing pigeons for part of their news reporting. In the early years of Reuter's, in the mid-19th century, they formed a fairly reliable live telex service.

Military pigeons

Military pigeons were in use until during the Korean War, by which time refined electronics had been employed for some time in communications. This function of communication was then already many centuries old. As well as being a means of troop communication, already referred to, besieged cities maintained contact with the outside world using homing pigeons right up to the present century. Well-known examples are the 'winged messengers' used during the sieges of Haarlem and Leiden in the 16th century. The siege of Paris in 1870 saw many hundreds of birds in action. Their activities were so important that every pigeon fancier whose birds took part in the hostilities was allotted a sentry for his loft. The reports the pigeons carried to and fro had a tremendous effect on the morale of army units and citizens.

During World War I great use was made of pigeons for military purposes. It is estimated that the German troops commandeered no less than one million Belgian pigeons. In Brussels there is a monument to the war effort of the fanciers and their birds. At Lille, in France, there is a memorial to the possibly 20,000 pigeons who lost their lives in the war.

Belgian, French, Italian and, later, British pigeons

Gunpowder *and* Pretty Baby, *two of the most famous military pigeons of World War I (top) and army 'convoyeurs' (attendants) in World War II.*

A memorial in Brussels to the contribution made by fanciers and their birds to the war of 1914–18.

distinguished themselves in carrying messages and other valuable material from hard-pressed positions. Equipped with ingeniously constructed twin-lens cameras, some birds took reconnaissance photographs of enemy targets and positions.

World War II

The museums in Washington, London and Hanover are full of mementoes of the flying war heroes from the Second War. There were pigeons which were decorated, buried with military honours, or set up in glass cases for modern visitors to admire. Names such as Lord Adelaide, President Wilson, Julius Caesar, Lady Astor, Jungle Joe and Burma Queen are indicative of their class, and ranks such as Captain Fulton their status. The birds that survived were provided with handsome quarters in which to spend their old age. At least 150 officers and 3,000 other ranks, members of the still extant United States Army Pigeon Service, were fully occupied with the American homing pigeons, which alone numbered over 54,000.

The birds also rendered services of a high order as a result of a careful training, in which some were trained to fly at night. They accompanied field patrols, naval squadrons and submarines. Parachutists took pigeons with them for dropping out of bombers. This was done with the aid of a simple paper bag with a hole in it. The time needed by the pigeon to free itself from the bag was sufficient to prevent it becoming the victim of the suction from the aircraft. Some members of this living flying brigade returned to their mobile base with a leg shot to pieces or a badly damaged wing, but with their valuable microfilms or code messages intact. The British pigeon, Mary, was wounded no less than 22 times during the five years that she flew on all the Allied fronts. The bird was awarded the Dickin Medal, the animal Victoria Cross, became a casualty and was recovered, smothered in wounds.

The German troops also understood the value of the homing pigeon, although there is no precise information about their use. Estimates of the number of pigeons employed at the height of the hostilities at the SS Pigeon Service in Berlin alone are put at 50,000, with some 600 to 800 handlers. Pigeons belonging to fanciers both in

A British paratrooper and pigeon (top).
Mobile pigeon loft of the 1950s (centre) and carrier pigeon equipment used by the Allied forces in 1940–45.

Carrier pigeons are still in active service with the Swiss army as a vital component of the communications troops. Top, pigeon with message tube. Left, equipment for transporting the birds.

Germany itself and in the occupied territories were commandeered or placed under military control.

Efficient means of communication
During the Korean War baskets full of well-trained homing pigeons were transferred to the Far East. The birds accompanied every patrol. One may ask why they continued to be used at a time when apparently perfect means of communication were available. The head of the intelligence service in Korea, Colonel Cooper, holds decided views about this. He points to the great expense of setting up technical means of communication in every part of the war zone. Besides: 'The greater the technical advances and the greater the perfection of radio transmission, the more refined will be the means of wholly or partly jamming or interfering with the transmissions. Carrier pigeons have proved during two world wars that nothing or nobody can stop them getting through, no matter how terrifying the circumstances. We can always take them with us and they are always ready to carry out their task. They are the cheapest means of communication imaginable.'

Origins
The long history of the pigeon, in which there are still many gaps, tells us nothing about the type of bird that was flown many centuries ago. One thing is certain, however: they were not the same birds as the athletes of today. It is almost universally agreed that the rock dove (Columbia livia) is the remote ancestor of all the birds we now call pigeons. The rock dove is still found in the regions around the Mediterranean Sea, which are also the source of the historical records and the stories of the more or less tame pigeons. Its sexual behaviour, external characteristics and pattern of flight show great similarities with the same characteristics of the domesticated specimens. Moreover, the rock dove

One of the many types of loft which the modern pigeon fancier has erected for his feathered friends.

which lives in the wild is certainly not afraid of Man and readily mates with 'our' pigeon.

It was probably the Egyptians, Greeks, Persians and neighbouring peoples who tied the rock dove to their homes and quite soon took up deliberately breeding. The evolution which leads to changes in the organs and in physical form requires a lot of time, in any event, much longer than the 180 years of the modern, more detailed history of the pigeon which is familiar to us. The Crusades played an important part in the diffusion of the pigeon over Europe.

From the Middle Ages the pigeon became an increasingly familiar element in the West European landscape. Many dovecots were built, particularly in France, in which up to 500 pigeons could be housed. These sturdy constructions, thousands of which were demolished during the French Revolution, served as shelter for the birds, which were kept mainly for their droppings. This privilege was one of the 'manorial rights' deriving from the possession of a manor. The dovecot, which formed part of the castle or manorial buildings, dominated the surrounding area and showed the populace where lay the centre of power. The common man was not allowed to build accommodation for pigeons!

Liège, Antwerp and Brussels types

The direct development towards the present racing pigeon began in around 1800. Present at the 'cradle' were Tumblers, Pouters, Carriers, Turbits and Highfliers. Over a period of 70 years three types emerged: the Liège type, small black birds with a short beak, a frill on the breast, powerfully built and with dark eyes; the Antwerp type, a large bird standing high on its legs and with an elongated head with well-developed nostrils and eyes from chestnut brown to nearly white; the Brussels type, broad and short with a thick head and large beak wattles.

This whole complex of pigeon lofts belongs mainly to Saturday fliers, the so-called 'pigeon garden'. It was built as an answer to the problems experienced by flat-dwellers in finding a spot among the increasing amount of high-rise building for their pigeons to call home.

This was the general line in the Belgium of those days, but there were also numerous intermediate forms, such as Ghent Pouters (which were introduced on flights from Tours in as early as 1815) crossed with Liège Shortbills, Tumblers with Smerles, Pigmy Pouters, Liège Pigeons or English Bills. A development took place within the three main types and through cross-breeding between them, from large pigeons with strong bones, which were good for long distances, but had little speed, towards medium-sized and smaller types which coupled endurance with speed. This development is, in fact, continuing to the present day.

The foundation for the present sport in the Netherlands was laid with pigeons imported from Belgium, birds of the Antwerp, Ghent and Brussels types. One thing is certain, it is no longer a 'manorial right' for the privileged individual, but rather a glorious challenge for everyone to distinguish him or herself in the sport.

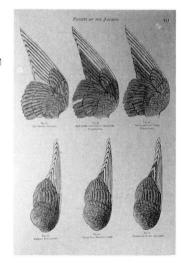

Delicate illustrations from an English publication of the mid-18th century showing detailed studies of variously coloured flight feathers.

Four English pigeons which took part in races in the period around 1875.

Other pigeons

Reference has already been made above to various other 'species' of pigeons apart from racing pigeons. Although the subject of this book is 'racing pigeons' and these are the ones which are by far the most numerous, their relatives are too interesting for them to be overlooked in this introduction. We shall restrict ourselves to the fancy and other show pigeons.

Readers in the possession of a crossword dictionary will know that no less than 250 entries are to be found under the heading 'pigeons'. The great majority of them are fancy pigeons. There are 200 recognised races in the Netherlands alone: Helmet pigeons, The Hague Highfliers, Capuchines, Highfliers, Shield Croppers and varieties graced with the names of breeders. All these races are divided into groups, such as Coloured, Trumpeter, Flesh, Wattle, Dewlap and Swift pigeons. They include such splendid representatives as the colourful Nuremberg Lark, the self-willed Councillor, the dignified Saxon Magpie Pouter and the imposing Norwich Cropper.

Whereas with the fancy pigeons it is the handsome appearance that counts, with pigeons such as Rollers and Tipplers we are concerned with a true flying sport.

The achievements and the judging generally take place within the vicinity of the loft. The aim is to keep the pigeons in the air for as long as possible and at such a height that they are visible only as tiny dots. As their name suggests, Tumblers occasionally turn somersaults during flight, while Rollers do so repeatedly. The world record for staying in the air – over 20 hours – is held by an English Tippler. Whole books can be, and have been, written about these races; the intention of these few lines is only to place the racing pigeon within the context of the hobby of pigeon fancying as a whole.

The bird

The free flight of racing pigeons appeals
strongly to our imagination. The slender
body seems to have so little trouble in
achieving something that must demand
strength and the unerring interplay of
body and brain.

Cock or hen?

Even the most experienced fancier will admit that it is particularly difficult to determine the sex of young racing pigeons since there are no external sex organs as with mammals. We should really just wait, because a moment will arrive when we shall know whether it is a cock or a hen, but in our inquisitiveness we devise all kinds of 'methods' to find an answer to this intriguing question. They feature regularly in the technical literature: the swinging of the wedding ring on a piece of string or, more seriously, the difference between the upper and lower labia pudenda with seven-day-old pigeons; or the length of the toes; or the reaction of the tail when the young pigeon is held in a certain way. There are more such fables in a sport which has living creatures as its subject . . .

It is nonsense that with female birds the right toe is shorter than the left. The only certainty, if we want one, is provided by the theory of heredity, namely that colour inheritance is sex-linked. This enables us to make more meaningful pronouncements about sex with regard to certain pairings on the basis of colour. All blue and chequered birds from red and dun hens, for example, will likewise be hens. (See also Heredity, p. 132). For the rest we have to rely on external characteristics and behaviour when the birds become a little older. With late-maturing breeds it may be many months before the sex can be determined with certainty.

The cock

The cock is usually sturdily built. The primary flight feathers, at the extremity of the wing, are broad. The cock is pugnacious and stalwart, more impudent and high-spirited than his sister and fond of paying court to the hens. He is continually engaged in extending his territory.

Head of a cock

A good example of the head of a cock bird. The eye ceres and beak wattles of the cock are often more developed than those of the hen.

Sexual organs

Drawings of the internal reproductive organs of a cock. On the left the *testes* in a dormant state; on the right in full production for the manufacture of *spermatozoa* (reproductive cells). The extremely thin *vas deferens* (seed tube) leads to the cloaca. In the drawing the kidneys are shown in blue. They are also connected with the cloaca for the evacuation of waste products.

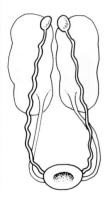 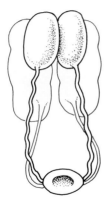

The hen

The majority of hens are more finely and slimly built than the cock. The head is smaller and the beak wattles and eye ceres are also more modest. The primary flight feathers are generally narrower than the cock's. The behaviour of the hens is characterised by solicitousness, particularly when there are young in the nest. They will defend the little family with great devotion. Hens generally enjoy the advances of a sturdy cock and they show their best side, dragging their tails and nodding their heads. At such moments even chance visitors to the loft have no difficulty in distinguishing the cocks from the hens.

If hens are separated from cocks for a long time they often have a tendency to enter into mutual relationships. The effect of the hormones may sometimes be so great that egg production begins, although these eggs will obviously be infertile. We shall see how an end can be put to what most fanciers regard as an undesirable situation, or how it can be prevented from happening at all.

Head of a hen

The head of the hen illustrated above is markedly finer in comparison with that of the cock illustrated opposite. Cocks and hens also sometimes differ in having more and less developed eye ceres and beak wattles, but, as both illustrations show, this is certainly not always the case. The disappearance of this kind of external difference between the two sexes has become particularly noticeable during the last few decades as a result of the tendency towards refinement of the racing pigeon type.

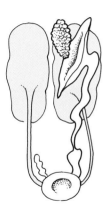
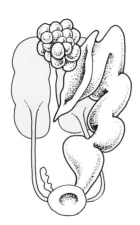

Sexual organs

The internal reproductive organs (gonads) of the hen. One of the two original ovaries is always lost when the bird is still a chick. When an egg follicle ripens the sac bursts and the ovum is sucked into the oviduct. The reproductive organs of both the cock and the hen are dormant for part of the year (left). As the brooding season approaches they become enlarged (right).

A cock in condition puts on a display (small photograph), especially if there is a hen around. He helps to look after the family, but when the young ones are about twelve days old he begins to take an interest again in other females.

Characteristic behaviour of the hen is care for and, if necessary, defence of the nest. She does not let anyone or anything get in her way, not even a cock.

External characteristics

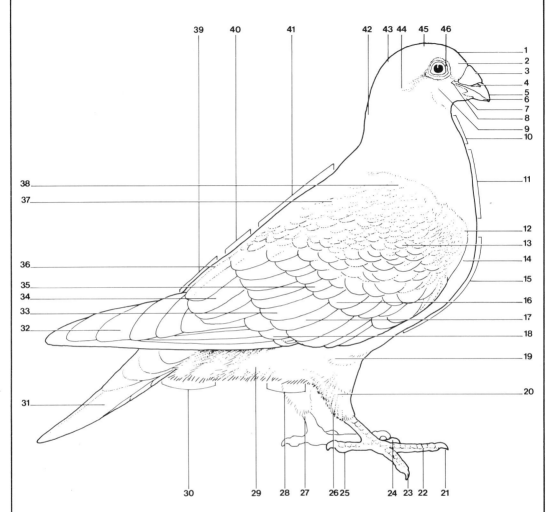

1. frontal
2. lore
3. nose cap
4. nasal cavity
5. upper mandible
6. lower mandible
7. gullet
8. malar region
9. auricular
10. gular region
11. jugular
12. wrist
13. smallest coverts
14. alula
15. breast feathers
16. lesser wing coverts
17. greater wing coverts
18. secondary flight feathers
19. flank
20. upper leg
21. claw
22. middle toe
23. outer toe
24. inner toe
25. hind toe (hallux)
26. heel
27. shank
28. abdomen
29. vent region
30. under-tail feathers
31. rectrices
32. primary flight feathers
33. secondary flight feathers
34. first wing band
35. lesser coverts
36. lesser mantle feathers
37. scapulars
38. shoulder
39. upper tail coverts
40. rump
41. back
42. nape
43. occiput
44. ear feathers
45. crown
46. eye cere

Colour distinctions

There is no relationship between the colour of a racing pigeon and its performance, which is why there is a great variety of colour among our birds. The comment 'even if he is purple, it makes no difference to me as long as he can fly well' hits the nail on the head. Colour is no criterion of selection when it comes to maintaining the standard of the loft. A rather different point is that many pigeon fanciers do not like to have a motley collection of birds. The majority prefer a degree of uniformity.

Two pigments determine the colour of racing pigeons: red and black. The absence of pigment gives white. In terms of heredity: certain genes determine how intense a colour will occur on a particular part of the pigeon's body. This is the origin of the chequered, blue-barred and grizzled types. All these pigeons possess black pigment, but it is more intense with some than with others.

Blue-barred

The basic pigment of the blue-barred breed is black. This breed also has numerous varieties. We find, for example, a complete or partial third bar. This marks the beginning of the transition from blue to chequered.

'Schallie'

The Schallie is erroneously associated with the Belgian Gebroeders Janssen (Arendonk) race. Neither Schallies nor the duns and the reds – on the whole – have black bills.

Blue/white-flighted

The lack of pigment in a particular feather tract gives white. The white-flighted has only a few white primary flight feathers. A pied bird also has a white head. There are, incidentally, also completely white birds.

Slated

The slated effect in a pigeon's plumage is the result of a less intensive black pigmentation than with a chequered bird.

Light chequered

The intensity of the underlying black determines whether a pigeon is lightly or heavily chequered. The photograph above shows a characteristically light chequered bird.

Red

Bars are also found with red birds, as is chequering. As always, these varieties reflect the intensity of the pigmentation. A true red is sometimes referred to as a 'fox'.

Black

A black racing pigeon is no relative of the crow as far as colouring is concerned. In pigeon circles black means the occurrence of very dark colouring in parts of the plumage.

Dark chequered

This is the dark representative of the chequered racing pigeons.

Light grey/grizzle

The lighter or darker character of the colouring of the grey pigeons is also determined by differences in intensity of pigmentation. This is a light grey example.

Dun/mealy

The underlying colour of a dun bird is red. The colour intensity is comparable with that of a blue-barred.

Dark grey

The black component is much stronger in this grey bird than in its companion in the photograph above. Grey and white pigeons are sometimes referred to as pieds.

Head

When they pick up a pigeon the majority of fanciers will first examine the head. They are assiduously looking for external features which betray the quality of the pigeon. At shows one hears such remarks as 'what a bright head, it radiates intelligence . . . an outstanding bird'. This conclusion is built on quicksand. What is inside the head cannot be read from the outside. But examining the head closely, looking at the pigeon face-to-face, is such a familiar picture that it is evidently a deep-seated need. And there is certainly no objection to it, as long as we know in our heart that enjoyment of the brightness and beauty confronting us is not the same as a measure of quality. It is no more than making a first acquaintance. A strong, somewhat larger beak is, of course, a better sign than a weak one, but it is no more than an indication, and then only for people who have had many birds pass through their hands.

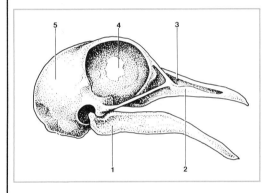

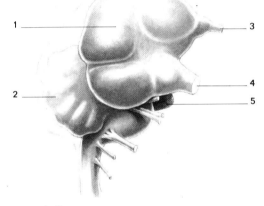

The structure of the head
1. lower mandible
2. upper mandible
3. nostril
4. orbit
5. cranium

1. cerebellum
2. cortex
3. olfactory nerve
4. optic nerve

5. pituitary gland, an important hormone producer

Beak wattles

The size of the beak wattles often depends on the variety of racing pigeon. The wattles of cocks are generally more coarsely developed than those of hens. There were once specimens with enormous beak wattles, but these have gradually been eliminated from the racing birds, whose wattles are more modest. Birds with – temporarily – scaly wattles (the pink flesh shows through the bottom layer) generally do not win competitions.

Shape

There is absolutely no relationship between the shape of a head and the quality of the bird in question. The average hen has a somewhat flatter head than her male companion. Although shape is a matter of taste, we like to see in an exhibition bird a handsome round head with a smooth transition to the curve of the beak. But birds with a more angular appearance can also be good fliers. On the left, an example of a somewhat flat head; on the right, a somewhat round head.

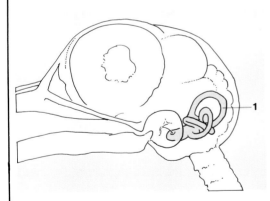

1. labyrinth
2. vertical canal
3. horizontal canal
4. cochlea

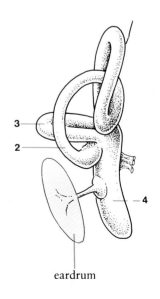

eardrum

Hearing and balance

A bird's ears serve not only to pick up familiar and unfamiliar sounds (sense of hearing), but have the second extremely important function of registering movements via the brain (sense of balance). We distinguish the outer and the middle ear, which receive and transmit the sound vibrations, and the inner ear where the actual functions are performed. The illustrations show the position of the organ in the head and an enlargement of the organ itself.

Eye

One of the most amusing sayings among pigeon fanciers, as far as eyes are concerned is: 'You can learn a lot from looking at pigeons' eyes, but you shouldn't have them in your own pocket.' That saying is right on the mark. It will certainly be some time before we have developed the ability to 'look in the mirror of the soul', so caution is called for in drawing firm conclusions about intelligence, health and breeding value after a cursory glance at the exterior of this sensory organ.

However this may be, we like to see a small pupil that is directed slightly forward. The structure of the iris should preferably be granular. If lines can be observed in it, the pigeon has carried the day with many fanciers. If there are numerous lines surrounding the pupil, the expression 'star eye' is sure to be heard.

Many fanciers attach great importance to what they call the eye-sign. What they are really seeing is the pigment layer of the inner side of the iris which becomes visible through the pupil opening at the front of the eye. This layer may be of a different colour from the pigment segment at the front, so that the eye-sign becomes visible in whole or in part.

The eye cere may be grey, white or pink. White ceres are preferred. Many fanciers do not like to see pink ceres, but this external characteristic is also completely irrelevant as far as a bird's performance is concerned. The colour of the eye ceres is related only to the variety of racing pigeon.

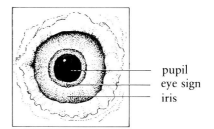

pupil
eye sign
iris

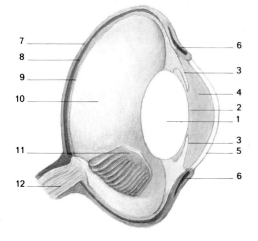

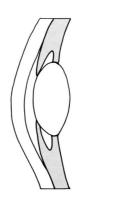 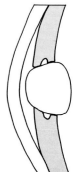

1. lens
2. pupil
3. iris
4. aqueous humour
5. cornea
6. eyelid
7. sclerotic
8. choroid
9. retina
10. vitreous humour
11. pecten
12. optic nerve

Eye adaptation

The eye is able to adapt itself to a greater or lesse intensity of light. The component which makes this adaptation possible is the pupil, which contracts in strong light and enlarges in poor light. This adaptation is a general biological phenomenon which also occurs with other animals and Man.

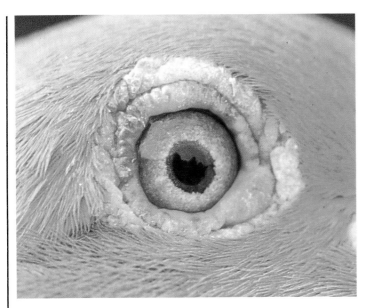

'The' eye

This is an example of the type of racing pigeon eye which most fanciers like to see. The eye sign surrounding the deep black pupil is clearly visible. The iris has a rich texture. This eye is also well enclosed.

Colours

All eye colours have produced both true champions and pigeons of little worth as far as the sport is concerned. The two eyes of a pigeon are sometimes not uniform in colour. As well as colour, the seating of the eye is important. We refer, therefore, to a 'loose' eye and an enclosed eye. Here are a few examples:

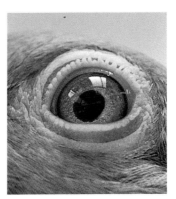

A so-called 'loose' eye: it is not properly enclosed by the eyelid (inside top).

Smerle eye: very dark; occurs mainly in pied birds.

A really handsome grey eye.

The pupil of this yellow-brown eye is somewhat enlarged at the bottom left, so that the bird seems to be squinting.

Brown eye with the eye sign partly distinguishable (top left and right).

Neck, back, shoulder, loins, rump

Pigeon fanciers prefer a broad, firm-feeling back. The rump, which is attached to it, must be well-filled and form a whole with the back. In other words, when we are holding the pigeon it must not feel as though it consists of two parts.

The rump is also the location of the gland which plays an important part in the maintenance of the feathers. The tail gland secretes a fatty substance which the pigeon distributes over its feathers with its beak, so that they remain water-repellant.

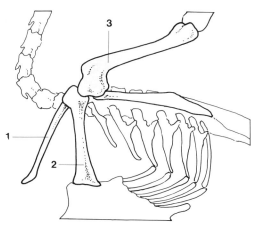

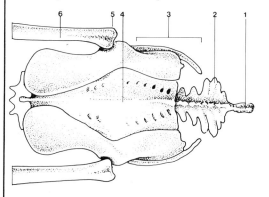

Shoulder

1. clavicle (wishbone)
2. coracoid
3. humerus

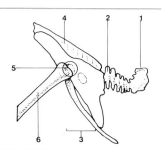

1. ploughshare
2. free caudal vertebrae
3. pelvis
4. synsacrum
5. hip
6. femur

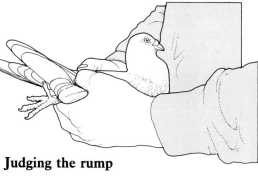

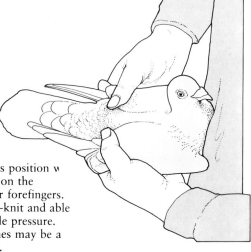

Judging the rump

It is important when judging the rump that the bird should be held comfortably in the hand, in a relaxed manner and not too tightly. We then exercise a light pressure on the back with both thumbs and slide them down to the rump without relaxing the pressure. From this position w feel the tail bones on the underside with our forefingers. They must be well-knit and able to withstand a little pressure. With hens the bones may be a little less well-knit.

Legs

We must realise that when we see a pigeon sitting only a small section of its legs is visible. This is the shank, to which the ring is attached. It often happens that a pigeon returns home with a broken leg. The shank can be fitted with a splint, but it is impossible for the layman to fit one to the shin or upper leg. Spontaneous healing is possible if the victim is placed in a separate loft. Later, the position of the leg will betray that the bird has been in collision with an obstacle, although this need not form any hindrance to flight.

Clipping

Some racing pigeons are troubled by claws which go on growing. These need to be clipped, but not shorter than about 10 mm, because there are blood vessels at the base of the claws.

Excessively thick legs

This pigeon's leg is so thick that the ring ought to be removed; otherwise there is a real danger that the leg will later have to be amputated. Through our club or association we can make contact with the national league or provincial branch to enquire what to do about the bird's identity now that it is without a ring. A stamp is usually placed on its wing, which has to be renewed annually.

Feathering

Strongly feathered legs, as in the photograph above, are probably a throwback to a fancy pigeon race. Feathering again does not have anything to do with quality. Prevent the ring becoming fixed in position by regularly cleaning the leg at the position of the ring. This can be done, for example, by moving a piece of string up and down between the leg and the ring.

Wing and feather

Little imagination is needed to establish that the wings are among the most important parts of the racing pigeon. They carry the bird over great distances and through sometimes difficult conditions. They must give the fancier an advantage over his colleagues. But however important the wings may be, other qualities are needed, both mental and physical, to achieve success. Each at its own level.

A good wing

The racing pigeon's wing has given rise to such violent differences of opinion that good friendships have been ruined over it. A yardstick is needed to determine whether a bird will be good at 250 km or 500 km. Bernouilli's theorem (the sum of potential energy and kinetic energy is constant) is applied to explain the physical phenomenon of lift. Charel Vanderschelden devoted practically the whole of his life to the study of the racing pigeon's wing, while Victor Vansalen did good work by adopting a scientific approach to the wings.

Under these circumstances, who would dare to define an ideal wing? And doesn't experience show that high speeds can be achieved with all kinds of wings? In any event, fanciers like to see the following characteristics: a narrow, rectilinear hind wing; a first primary flight feather which projects relative to the hind wing; the four last primary flights forming a separate group; and a good rounding of the final feathers (an old-fashioned knife shape). When the pigeon is handled the feathers must feel silky and glide through the hand, so to speak. The latter certainly has a lot to do with the health of the bird in question.

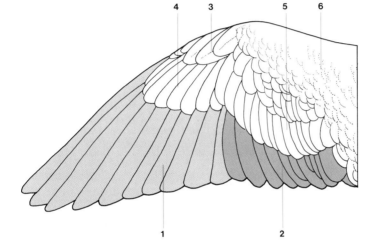

Structure

1. primary flight feathers
2. secondary flight feathers
3. alula
4. wing coverts
5. wing coverts
6. scapulars

This young pigeon will acquire a handsome plumage in a few days. Sometimes the feathers do not emerge properly from the shaft, in which case it is helpful to moisten the shaft.

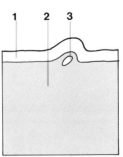 

Development of a down feather

With down feathers the barbs grow longitudinally. When the feather is fully grown the food supply from the centre of the sheath ceases. The sheath breaks open and the barbs emerge.
1. epidermis
2. dermis
3. papilla of follicle
4. sheath
5. barbs

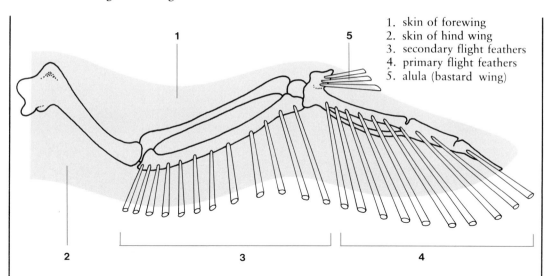

1. skin of forewing
2. skin of hind wing
3. secondary flight feathers
4. primary flight feathers
5. alula (bastard wing)

Cross-section of humerus

This bone is hollow as are various other bones in the pigeon. On the left is a longitudinal cross-section, on the right a transverse cross-section of the humerus.

Flight feather

1. proximal umbilicus
2. vane
3. fret mark
4. hyprorachis
5. soft barbules/fluff
6. outer vane
7. quill
8. inner vane

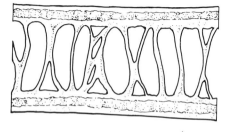

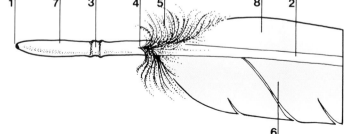

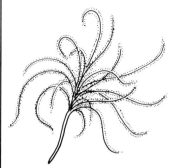

Barbs and hooks

The hooks serve to lock the barbs together, thus creating a web which is firm but flexible. A split web can be effortlessly restored by a preening bird.

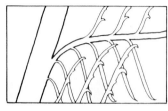

Down feathers

Down feathers maintain the temperature of the bird's body. They do not have a quill and the barbs are not provided with hooks, but they intermesh together.

Frill or jabot

The Cropper blood of the old Antwerp pigeon, ancestor of the modern racing pigeon, sometimes still asserts itself in the frill. This is an out-of-line area of feathers on the breast.

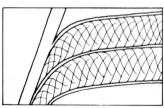

Into the air with the aid of the wings and thanks to the streamlining of the body.

How it works

The difference between the speed at which the air passes over the convex upper side and the concave under side of the wings creates an upwards pressure. As it rises the pigeon changes the angle of the wing in relation to the airstream. By spreading the alula, which is comparable to an elevator, the airflow above the wing is restored.

49

Vital functions

On the following pages some of the normal phenomena of the pigeon's life will be discussed: moulting, respiration and blood circulation. Other physiological processes, such as ovulation and digestion will be dealt with under breeding and feeding. Both there and here it will become clear how finely the organs are attuned to each other.

Moulting

The plumage is exposed to all kinds of weather conditions which adversely affect its quality. Moreover there may be 'mechanical' defects, such as a broken feather, so that it is an advantage that nearly all the feathers are renewed annually. (The secondary feathers, however, are not always renewed in a single year, but generally only three at a time with young pigeons.) The renewal of the feathers takes place gradually, so that the birds can continue flying. Nevertheless, there is a certain period in the year, the moult, when the whole plumage seems to be shaken out. During this very important period of the pigeon year, which reaches its climax in August and September, the foundation is laid for the new flying season. The birds will have less wish to fly during these months, even though it is still possible for them to do so. Only after the second moult is it possible to make a correct assessment of the wing. The wing pattern of young pigeons is unpredictable and is not always fixed, even with yearlings.

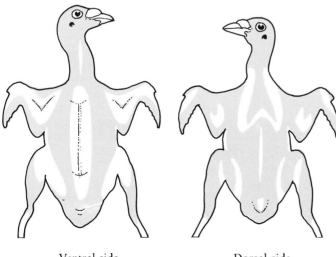

Ventral side   Dorsal side

Feather tracts

The feathers emerge from the skin and cover the whole of the pigeon's body. They do not grow everywhere, however, but are arranged in so-called feather tracts. The position of the tracts is such that the joints can operate freely and the pigeon is not restricted in its movements.

Down moult

As well as the main moult, pigeon fanciers have also to deal with the moulting of the down feathers. This moult takes place throughout the year, but there are times when the fancier will find more down than usual in the lofts, such as during brooding and when the widower cocks are beginning to come into form. The down moult may also stop quite suddenly, such as when sickness or extreme exertion upset a bird's ordinary rhythm. Down moult is therefore a good measure of the state of wellbeing of the loft. It provides the fancier with visible 'proof' that the different vital functions are proceeding properly.

Moulting schedule

This is the moulting schedule of a young pigeon born in March. The figure against the index number of each feather indicates the number of days after birth.

Feather number	left	right
1.	169	169
2.	146	147
3.	132	132
4.	117	117
5.	104	104
6.	89	90
7.	87	87
8.	72	72
9.	66	66
10.	45	45
11.	112	113
12.	219	220
13.	228	230
14.	220	220
15.	184	184
16.	215	215
17.	211	210
18.	158	158
19.	129	130
20.	93	93
21.	128	128
22.	165	165
23.	147	148
24.	136	136
25.	92	100
26.	128	128

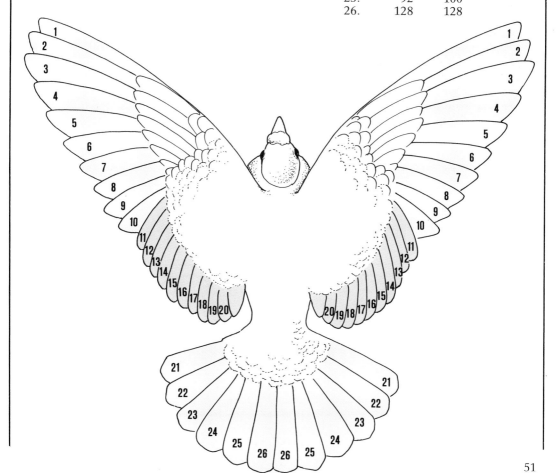

Induced moulting

Human intervention in the natural process of moulting is possible. We can accelerate the process, but also, as is explained on the next page, delay it. Induced moulting can be achieved by a number of ways. In the first place, the eggs are removed from brooding birds. The birds are then given a mild purgative to purge them internally, after which they are starved for a day and then fed with a mixture containing a high proportion of oil-bearing seeds. If the loft is also warm and light, the fancier will soon see the feathers drifting around. It is clear that with this method there is no question of a gradual moult; birds treated in this way cannot immediately be entered in races.

This method is sometimes used to enable birds which still have to rear a chick at a late stage quickly to make up their leeway in the moult. Some fanciers who are specialised in the game with young pigeons also use this method to enable young birds which have virtually completed their moult to participate in the major races.

The first step towards induced moult: the removal of the eggs.

Light regulation

A useful piece of equipment in the loft is an automatic light switch with a time clock. This equipment makes it possible, particularly during the winter, for the birds to have sufficient time to drink after their meal. In order to avoid excessively fast moulting, however, it is advisable to be sparing with artificial light.

If the ears are exposed, the birds should on no account be allowed to race.

Delayed moult

The opposite of the induced moult is the delayed moult, which is employed for some of the races for young pigeons, particularly those in August and September.

Those fanciers who choose the delayed moult exploit for the purpose one of the characteristics of this physiological process: birds which sit for 14 days cease moulting. Accordingly young cocks and hens which are rearing a squeaker in the nest bowl will have a good plumage and a good plumage means good flying (depending, of course, on the young bird's potential). A further factor, as will be discussed in detail later, is that parent birds will have an additional motive for returning home as soon as possible, because that is where their offspring are waiting.

Another way to delay the moult is to darken the loft to exclude the light which activates the moult. It is for the fancier to decide whether he wishes to make use, regularly or otherwise, of such an intervention in a natural process. It is often most sensible to let nature take its course, both as far as the induced and the delayed moult are concerned.

Darkening

With the aid of a roller blind or a few pieces of cardboard we can admit more or less light into the pigeon loft.

During the moult

In addition to losing its feathers, the pigeon also loses some of its beauty during the moult, but with proper care and feeding the moult will proceed smoothly and the bird's appearance will be rapidly restored to its former splendour.

Respiration

Birds, including the pigeon, lead an active life. They are visibly active, but there are also invisible processes at work which consume a great deal of energy. Food is an important source of energy, but the pigeon, like all birds, also possesses a special respiratory system which makes this active life possible.

Respiration is the means of supplying oxygen to the blood. The air is carried via the bill or the nostrils to the throat and from there via the windpipe to the air sacs. These force the air into the lungs. In these relatively small organs – the dimensions of which are fully compensated by the size of the air sacs – the oxygen is delivered to the blood. Carbon dioxide which is released by combustion in the cells is returned by the blood to the lungs.

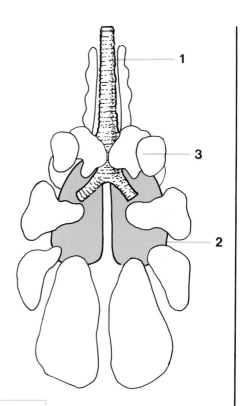

Syrinx

This is the vocal organ of the pigeon. The air passing out of the lungs sets the membrane vibrating, thus generating a sound.

1. muscle
2. trachea
3. bronchus
4. bladder, filled with mucus
5. membrane

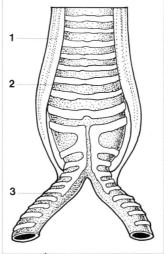

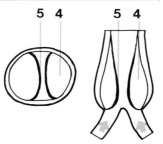

1. trachea
2. lungs
3. air sacs

Air sacs

The pigeon has a rigid rib cage and no diaphragm. In the centre of the body are the unique organs called the air sacs. Their expansion and contraction ensures that the air is forced into the lungs. They also have a cooling function. In contrast to most mammals, the pigeon does not sweat. Heat is absorbed by the air sacs and expelled through the open beak by panting. Lastly, the air sacs give the pigeon a low specific gravity in relation to its bulk.

Functions of the blood and temperature

One of the functions of the blood is the supply of oxygen and nutrients and the discharge of carbon dioxide and waste products. It can fulfil this function properly only if it is continually circulating through the body. The circulation takes place through the blood vessels. The 'driving pump' for this is the heart which propels the blood through the arteries. The latter terminate in capillaries where the exchange takes place. The same circuit is also used for the return journey. A pigeon's heart beats at a rate of about 200 pulses a minute, rising to 400. Partly because of this the bird has a higher body temperature than Man, namely 41°C.

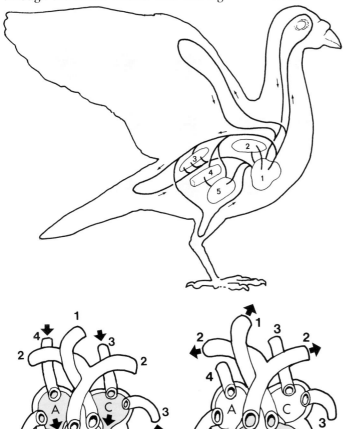

Blood circulation

Arteries carry oxygenated blood from the heart through the body. The release of oxygen takes place in the capillaries. The veins then return the deoxygenated blood to the heart and from there to the lungs to receive fresh oxygen.
1. heart
2. lungs
3. kidneys
4. intestines
5. liver

Greater circulation

The oxygenated blood enters the left ventricle (D) and is pumped into the arteries via the aorta (1). The blood then flows throughout the body, exchanging food and oxygen for waste products and carbon dioxide, and eventually returns via the veins (4) to the right atrium (A). This is where the lesser circulation recommences.

Lesser circulation

The deoxygenated blood enters the right atrium (A) via the veins (4). It continues its passage to the right ventricle (B) from where it is pumped by the heart to the lungs via the pulmonary artery (2). In the lungs an exchange takes place, with carbon dioxide being given up in return for oxygen. The pulmonary vein (3) then carries the oxygenated blood to the left atrium (C).

1. aorta (main artery)
2. pulmonary artery
3. pulmonary vein
4. artery

A. right atrium
B. right ventricle
C. left atrium
D. left ventricle

36
35
34
33
32
31
30
29
28
27
26
25
24
23
22
21
20
19
18
17
16
15
14
13

1
2
3
4
5
6
7
8
9
10
11
12

The skeleton of the pigeon

1. skull
2. occipital bone
3. orbit
4. nasal cavity
5. lower mandible
6. culmen
7. cervical rib
8. clavicles (wishbone)
9. coracoid
10. sternum
11. keel
12. toe phalanges
13. hallux
14. tarsometatarsus
15. heel
16. tibiotarsus
17. fibula
18. pelvis
19. ischium
20. ploughshare
21. free caudal vertebrae
22. femur
23. synsacrum
24. ilium
25. ribs
26. scapula
27. thoracic vertebrae
28. humerus
29. elbow
30. ulna
31. radius
32. wrist
33. carpometacarpal
34. metacarpal
35. finger
36. finger phalanx

Skeleton

The primary function of the skeleton is to give rigidity to the body. It also protects certain important organs, such as the heart, lungs, brains and eyes. It further serves as a point of attachment for the various groups of muscles.

The bones of the wing, in particular, are hollow and filled with air. This gives the bird an appreciable weight saving. Other bones contain marrow in which the various blood cells are manufactured. The most striking component of the pigeon's skeleton is the breastbone.

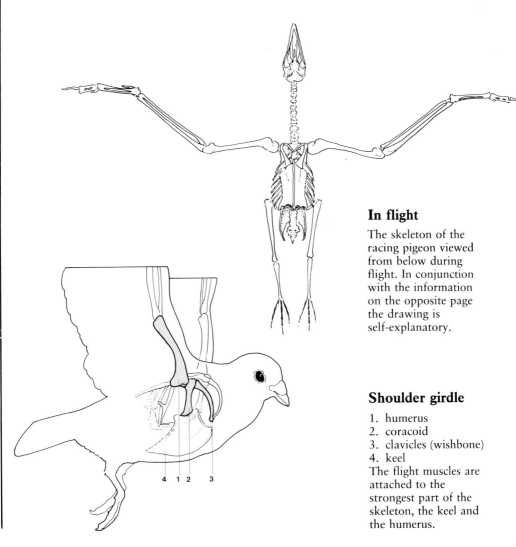

In flight

The skeleton of the racing pigeon viewed from below during flight. In conjunction with the information on the opposite page the drawing is self-explanatory.

Shoulder girdle

1. humerus
2. coracoid
3. clavicles (wishbone)
4. keel

The flight muscles are attached to the strongest part of the skeleton, the keel and the humerus.

Muscles

The ability of muscles to contract enables the body to move. Two kinds of muscles can be distinguished: smooth and striped. Smooth muscles are so constructed that they can contract slowly, while striped muscles are able to contract quickly.

The most interesting of the striped muscles for racing pigeon fanciers are the flight muscles, which are clearly recognisable as the greater and lesser pectorals. Together these muscles account for no less than half the total weight of muscle and for about a fifth of the total weight of the bird. They are also a delicacy for the many people who eat pigeons.

In judging a pigeon's musculature attention must be paid to the suppleness and length of the great pectoral muscle, which should be as long as possible.

Muscle bundles

The great pectoral muscle occupies a prominent place in the pigeon's body. The size of the muscle can be clearly seen in the illustration.

Great pectoral muscle

The great pectoral muscles are attached to the lowest part of the keel, to the edges of the sternum (breastbone) and to the clavicles (wishbone) and run from here to the top of the humerus. With good fliers the colour is deep red because of the large supply of blood needed to perform the strenuous work.

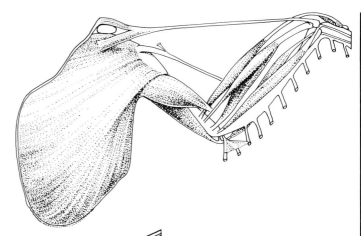

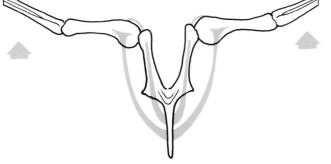

The lesser pectoral muscles move the wings upwards, an activity for which very little strength is required.

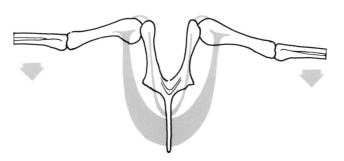

The large size of the great pectoral muscles is explained by the great burst of energy which they must produce to bring the wings down.

Leg muscle

The relatively small leg muscles control the movements of the pigeon's leg. The tendon is the tough inelastic part of the muscle which has grown together with the bone. It can be seen from the drawing that the tendon causes the curving of the toe phalanges.

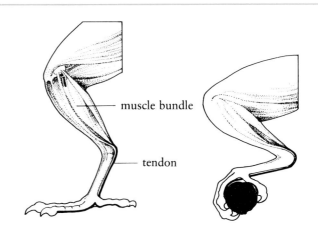

muscle bundle

tendon

Handling and judging

The judging of racing pigeons is an essential part of the contact between practitioners of the sport. One can often already tell from the owner's eyes and the way in which he hands you the bird that a particular pigeon is the favourite of the loft. One fancier obviously has a better judging instinct than another, but no one can really see into a pigeon. Nevertheless, we are convinced that we must breed in a particular direction in order to progress. What these qualities should be and how we are to observe them is dealt with extensively in this book.

Aside from this, judging has become a quite self-contained part of the sport. It takes place at the annual winter shows. The majority of fanciers regard it as a pleasant way of passing the time during the off-season, while others concentrate on the breeding of fancy racing pigeons. This difference in approach to the show pigeon makes it desirable to separate the racing pigeon class from the exhibition class at shows, although there are specialists who are able to breed an ideal type of pigeon (= standard pigeon) which can also win prizes at racing.

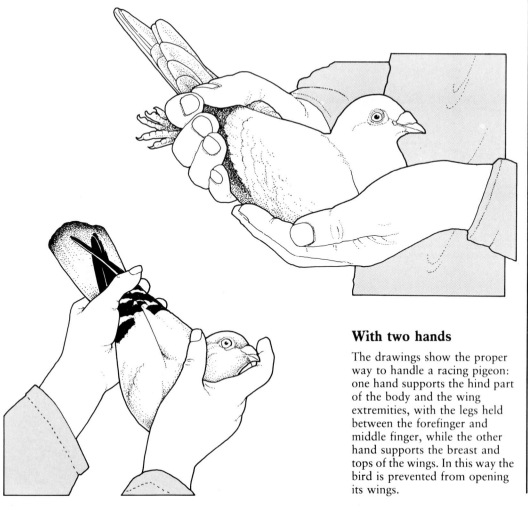

With two hands

The drawings show the proper way to handle a racing pigeon: one hand supports the hind part of the body and the wing extremities, with the legs held between the forefinger and middle finger, while the other hand supports the breast and tops of the wings. In this way the bird is prevented from opening its wings.

Wing

The size of wing must be appropriate to the bird. Some pigeons do not allow their wings to be held readily. This is often related to their obstinate nature, although some experts consider that it reflects an absence of flexibility.

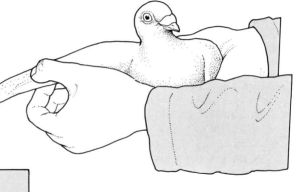

Pectoral muscles

The illustration shows how the pigeon should be held for judging the great pectoral muscles. The length of the muscle is determined by running the fingertips slowly along the keel from front to rear. The longer the fingers feel resistance from what fanciers sometimes call the 'inflated inner tube', the longer the pectoral muscle. The suppleness of the muscles is judged by moving them to and fro sideways between the fingertips. With plump birds it is very difficult to determine the quality of the muscles.

Eyes

This is the commonest way of holding a pigeon to examine its eye. This is how we try to look into the bird's soul, but unfortunately . . . it never betrays its qualities. Looking at the bird's head from the front, we like to see the gaze directed forwards, to the extent that it even appears a little cross-eyed.

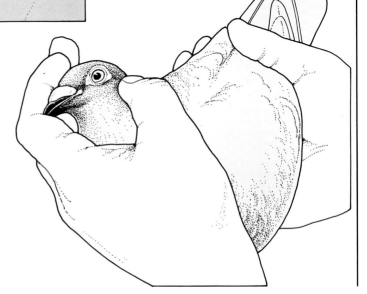

The standard

The Dutch Group of Certificated Judges was established in 1925 and drew up a specification to which the ideal pigeon should conform. The specification deals only with external characteristics and says nothing about flight ability. The standard has been changed over the years and adapted to the appearance of good modern fliers. The nice thing is that the majority of good fliers acquit themselves quite well when judged by this standard. With general, and therefore somewhat relative, descriptions such as 'good, firm, handsome', it is not surprising that judges differ among themselves about the finer points. There is no official 'group' of judges in Belgium although in 1984 a Belgian, who was incidentally also the first woman, took the examination in the Netherlands.

To the show

Exhibitors must enter well prepared birds, which must be healthy, clean, not fat, have no serious defects and be in good condition. But bear in mind the well-known saying among fanciers: 'showing is a disappointment'.

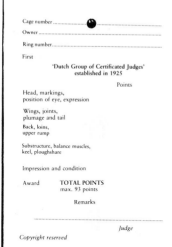

Cage number .... •‍ ....

Owner ....

Ring number...

First

'Dutch Group of Certificated Judges' established in 1925

Points

Head, markings, position of eye, expression

Wings, joints, plumage and tail

Back, loins, upper rump

Substructure, balance muscles, keel, ploughshare

Impression and condition

Award   TOTAL POINTS
max. 93 points

Remarks

....

Judge

Copyright reserved

Judging label

The points vary from 17 to 18.5 for each feature, with the exception of a single 19. The maximum number of points which can be scored is 93 for old pigeons, 92.5 for young birds and 91.5 for late breds on three-year-old feathers. For the Olympiade there is an international standard with a different division of features and points.

A joy to behold. It is perfectly possible for beauty and excellence to be combined, as in this pigeon whose beauty and achievements allowed her to participate in the international Olympiade in Tokyo (see page 240).

Housing

Good accommodation is vital for the
pigeon's health and is indispensable for
successful racing. This chapter gives
hints both for builders and for the
owners of existing pigeon lofts.

The whys and wherefores of loft building

Noblesse oblige, it is sometimes said. To translate that into pigeon racing terms: we must accept the consequences of keeping livestock in or close to our own home. We must accept the demands which are the result of our intervention in the natural course of events, although this intervention was not and is not made at the expense of the birds. They do not willingly accept the sometimes long flight 'home' for nothing, but they have become dependent on us. We have undertaken to care for them, to feed them, look after and house them. We do so not least in our own interest.

At the end of the book we take a peep into the pigeon fancier's accounts book. It might lead us to conclude that there are cheaper hobbies, but in providing the accommodation we can spend however much we choose. In the pigeon sport you don't necessarily get better value by spending more money. Sporting achievements cannot be bought, either by the purchase of expensive birds, or by providing lofts where the pigeons are, so to speak, provided with armchairs. Anyone who wishes to have luxury, whether in the erection of the building itself or in its fitting out, should not be deterred, but it is not the pigeons which demand the comfort. Numerous examples prove that champions – if that is what we are after – live in all possible kinds of structures, although they are all good lofts designed to meet the needs of the birds.

A home-made loft

Obviously, much more preparation time will be needed for a home-made structure than for the erection of a loft delivered in kit form. However, anyone who has old timber available can save money by building their own loft. The functions and requirements will have to be thought about carefully beforehand. Then there is the work of erection itself, and dependence on the weather, certainly in the early stages. To put it briefly, it is a challenge and a decreasing number of fanciers are accepting it.

The sketch

Every building project begins with a sketch which forms the basis of the working drawings. With this piece of paper we explore all the possibilities. What space do we have available? How far do our financial means reach? Do we have enough time, practical ability and imagination to put something together alone, or in cooperation with others? Do we have enough understanding of the needs of the birds to be able to provide for them ourselves? Or would it be better to buy a construction kit in which these needs have been met?

Construction kit

A wide range of kits of all sizes and kinds is now available in the trade. With the better makes considerable attention has been paid to the needs of the pigeons and the fancier's place in the structure. Our creative contribution to the kits is small, but they do relieve us in part of finding solutions to such problems as the access of air and light which constitute the secret of creating a suitable home for our pigeons.

Helping hands

are certainly easier to find when it is a question of erecting a ready-made loft than for a home-made structure. If a couple of one's fellow fanciers are willing to help, the loft can be put up in one day. There are many racing pigeon clubs in which the help of friends is a time-honoured custom. And who would argue that a ready-made loft of this kind, perhaps with the owner's own colour scheme, is not a palace for the birds?

Planning permission

When in Rome . . . This saying is also true when building pigeon lofts. The Dutch can be somewhat envious of the apparent ease with which their southern neighbours get their building plans passed. They tend to forget the higgledy-piggledy and sometimes lopsided structures which confront the train traveller in the centres of large Dutch cities, although these are gradually becoming a thing of the past. The Belgians can be a little envious in their turn of the more planning-minded approach of their northern neighbours. However this may be, Dutch fanciers who wish to build their own lofts will have to apply to the local authority.

In addition landlords often attach conditions to, or sometimes even forbid, the keeping of pigeons.

How, what and how much

may be built is laid down in development plans and building regulations. These generally leave little to chance. The regulations differ from one council to another and so it is not possible to give guidelines here about what size of loft may be built on a parcel size of so many square metres, nor about height, nor about the position in relation to the site boundaries. It is a good idea to go to the local council for advice, taking with you your own sketch plan or that of the manufacturer, before spending money on working drawings or the purchase of materials.

Some fanciers build their loft a little above the ground, on brick piers, for example. Their aim is to encourage the air circulation by giving the wind free play and so keep the loft dry. This is in contrast to current ideas about installing an insulating air layer under the floor as a means of combatting rising damp.

Headaches

Building regulations, or the wishes of petty bureaucrats, which limit the height of the roof can cause fanciers a lot of headaches. The loft in this photograph had a pitched roof, but it did not meet with the approval of the authorities. The only way to obtain planning permission was to remove the pitched roof and replace it with a lean-to.

The erection of lofts in residential areas often encounters many more difficulties than building one in a peaceful spot in the countryside.

Situation

The most ideal situation is not just there for the finding. Not only are there 'problems' from the neighbours, but there are the restrictions of the local authority or the landlord. There may be trees in the way, or there are only unfavourable spots remaining on the site where the loft is to be built. All fanciers agree that the ideal situation for the front of the loft is facing southeast. This enables the sun's rays to kill bacteria because the sun enters the loft at every moment of the day. But we can't always find such a situation.

Since an essential part of our hobby is to have a view of what the birds are doing, it is certainly no solution to build the loft with the back elevation to the house where this is the only way of achieving the ideal situation. Fortunately there are other solutions, such as roof-lights, sputniks (see p. 92) etc. Modern designs, with the glass being placed increasingly towards the top instead of in the front, clearly show the way things are going.

Wind and trees

It is recommended that when a new loft is built it should be exposed to the wind as far as possible. This promotes ventilation because the used air is sucked away through the open ridge described on page 71. Trees cause shade so if we have a choice, we should avoid a site near trees.

Shade

is an enemy of a healthy stock of pigeons. Sun gives warmth and light. It drives away damp. The quality of the light can be improved by so distributing the windows over the structure that the sun can do its useful work at every time of day. If local conditions make it impossible to orientate the front elevation with its glass towards the sun, the problem will have to be solved with glass roof lights. The flying compartments in any event should face into the sun.

Shallow lofts

may heat up quickly in the sun's rays. If there is insufficient ventilation and there are too many birds, they become too hot. With a relatively large area of glass large fluctuations of temperature will occur. These aspects can better be regulated with deeper lofts from, say, about two metres. Moreover, they make it easier for a bird to hide away in a quiet corner or to be alone, either as an individual or as a pair.

Functions of the loft

Fanciers build lofts for a number of reasons. They wish to be near their birds. They wish to be able to see the birds, look after them and so build up that relationship of trust which is so vital when the birds return from a flight. Fanciers also build because they make demands of their pigeons. As far as the pigeons themselves are concerned, they can manage with less, or even with almost nothing. They are still sufficiently close to their ancestors, the rock doves, to be able to get by with the very simplest accommodation, such as the simple niche in the wall which serves as a nesting place for the common urban pigeon. But we do not participate in competition flying with common urban pigeons . . .

We should also bear in mind that the fancier must feel at home in the loft as he spends part of every day with the birds. He must be able to move about without being in constant fear of banging his head. The loft must be so constructed and fitted out that he can devote his undivided attention to the care of the birds, to fetching and carrying for them and to cleaning their quarters.

On a large scale

With breeding stations such as this we are speaking of keeping pigeons on a large scale. Here the pigeons are kept for a living and great care has been given to the construction of the buildings, for example.

'Reception room' on a flat roof: high and well-situated. The right-hand picture is of a large aviary.

Requirements

The place where the racing pigeons are to feel at home must first of all be dry and well-ventilated. Some fanciers also regard good insulation and an even temperature as of equal importance. If a loft meets the basic requirements which he himself has laid down, the fancier will also feel very much at ease there. The list of requirements can also be approached from another, more negative, standpoint: what should be avoided? Pigeon fanciers sum this up as: chilliness, clamminess, cellar and cold, or the 4 Cs. The relative humidity must not exceed 70 per cent.

A loft must obviously be well-built and properly finished. Shoddiness will give rise to a lot of problems, such as draughts, leaks etc,

at a later date. The loft must obviously also be sensibly designed. A pigeon must be able to land freely and its owner should not have to bend every time he walks under the landing platform.

It is better not to have a flat roof. To put it plainly a fairly high-pitched roof encourages the birds to go in more quickly after a race. A high-pitched roof also creates a large reservoir of fresh air above the pigeons' heads. As many readers will know, a high-pitched roof has many structural advantages too, such as less maintenance and less likelihood of leaks. The pitch is made steeper at the front, so that the water drains off the back.

Glass

is placed as high as possible. We do not use more than is necessary to admit sufficient light. To give an ideal figure, the total area of glass amounts to one third of the front elevation, provided it is well positioned. Double glazing is not essential.

Dimensions

As has already been touched upon, sufficient depth is important in order to achieve a more even temperature and to give the birds the opportunity to be alone. When determining the height it is important that it is not so high that the birds can fly over our heads. Suitable dimensions for a free-standing loft are: width at the front ca. 3.5 m, depth 2 m and height to the gutter a little under 2 m.

Humidity

can be measured. A relative humidity of 70 per cent is an excellent average for a pigeon loft. If anyone considers it a bit excessive to buy a hygrometer, he should at least borrow one.

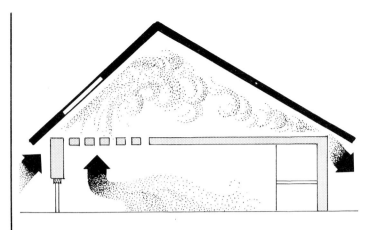

Foundations

The loft should be placed, if possible, on brick piers. With the most common type of loft, the garden loft, it is recommended that one should start with a brick-lined trench about one metre deep. This makes it possible to provide a sufficiently high-pitched roof to meet the requirements of many building regulations. It should incidentally be noted that many fanciers achieve excellent results with birds from lofts placed on four blocks, on kerbstones or . . . tiles

Ventilation

by means of an open ridge ensures that the used air, which naturally rises, flows out at the top. This makes possible the entry of fresh air from below. It is better to provide opening windows at the construction stage than to use ventilators.

The floor

consists of smoothly planed boards. Every joint can house pests which threaten the health of the birds, so regular cleaning can prevent a lot of harm. It is therefore also helpful to cover the floor with plywood.

Cavity walls

provide insulation by means of the still air filling the cavity between the inner and outer walls. It is also possible to provide insulation using products available in the trade. Fitting laths under the roof is preferable to insulating the attic.

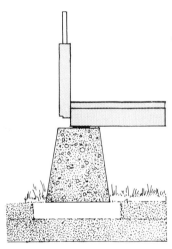

Overpopulation

as will be discussed in the chapter on veterinary matters, is very bad for pigeons. When designing the loft allow half a cubic metre per bird. Here, too, limitation (in the number of pigeons) reveals the master.

Building materials

Old, used timber is an excellent building material for lofts, whose primary requirement is dryness. If you do not have any timber lying about yourself, go in search of demolition timber. New timber, because it may warp, can give rise to leaks. (A matter of expansion and contraction.) A much greater objection is that gas may form in fresh timber. This is sometimes the reason why not very good flying results may be achieved from brand new and carefully built and equipped lofts. Hardboard may also be used.

Buyers must be careful not to buy board which smells when it is wet. A third material is plywood. It is perhaps unnecessary to point out that hardboard and plywood should be used only in the interior.

The design for a home-made loft can, of course, also be carried out in brick, although this is much more expensive and demands more technical skill. Experience has also shown that brick structures can give rise to problems when they are first built.

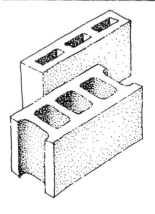

Hardboard is a good material for the interior, as is chipboard provided it does not give off any harmful fumes.

Window frames and glass in the front must allow the entry of the necessary light, although there are also other possibilities.

Bricks are an excellent building material, although not cheap.

Types of loft

On this and the following pages a review is given of the different kinds of loft in use among fanciers. Although the differences between some of the types are not very great and there are more garden lofts, for example, than all other types put together, we have decided to illustrate as many types as possible. This is for the sake of completeness and in order to make fanciers aware of the possibilities, irrespective of their own living conditions.

Garden loft

The most striking advantages of a garden loft are the possibilities for social contact and the easy accessibility. The fancier is able, at least if his loft is not too badly positioned, to see his pigeons, or at least some of them. And the other members of the family can see what he is up to. Moreover, the fancier can concentrate all his activities in one place, which avoids a lot of fetching and carrying, as happens with roof lofts. Garden lofts are situated in the midst of nature, so to speak. They are in immediate contact with the wind and with the sun, as far as the surrounding trees permit. That is an advantage, but damp also has free access. Something must be done about that disadvantage – and it can.

A foundation of air

Garden lofts account for by far the highest proportion of lofts but many owners have altered and added to them a great deal before they were really satisfied. Some of them even had to tackle the foundations of the loft before the achievements of the birds equalled the achievements of their lords and masters in the building sphere. Much of this effort was related to the removal of the fundamental disadvantage of this loft type: rising damp.

Anyone contemplating building a loft can learn from the experiences of his fellow fanciers. The weight of a garden loft is best carried if it is built directly on a levelled site and it is still better if the latter is provided with a layer of ready-mix concrete. But the climate is characterised by a lot of moisture which rises through the soil into lofts resting on the ground. The result is a clammy atmosphere, damp walls and, in the worst cases, mould. Scarcely anything can be done about this without resort to heating elements. They cost additional money and it is questionable whether they adequately solve the problem.

It may be better to provide for an additional air layer under the building, which can also serve as extra storage space. An air layer 20 to 30 cm deep is sufficient, but 50 cm would be the ideal. Even if the space is used for the storage of accessories, it is necessary to close it off, as otherwise the insulating effect will be lost. This provision has to

A rustic garden loft.

be paid for, of course, but the investment is certainly worth while.

Spreading a layer of quicklime under the floor of the loft is another way of dealing with the problem of rising damp and it also keeps away insects, such as ants.

Building high

If only a small area of land is available, or if the site has to be shared with other people, we can build high, provided it is allowed of course. The pigeons do not have the least objection to a two-storey home.

Come off the roof

Wire netting on the roof, sometimes put on at right angles, or a can on a piece of string are both intended to deter the pigeons from loitering, particularly after returning from a race.

Sliding doors

In most instances space in the loft will be at a premium. Sliding doors are a very practical solution to this problem.

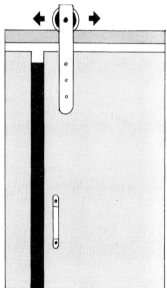

Roof covering

The choice of roof covering is governed by its insulating qualities. The range of temperature between day and night can be considerable in our climate, so that the roof must help to keep the temperature as even as possible. The old corrugated iron sheets did not do this. The asbestos sheeting which can be bought today is much better, certainly if it is supplemented by insulation. The best covering, however, is still the roofing tile. Obviously, we are referring to a pitched roof, which is really the best method for a garden loft.

The floor

of a garden loft may rest on massive foundations with an additional air layer, in which case it can be quite a light floor, such as boards covered with sheets of plywood. Under floors which rest more or less directly on the soil there should be laid on a layer of sand and rubble, with a 5-cm cement layer over that.

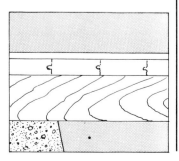

Roof loft

Roof lofts are quite common, particularly in Belgium. The amount of actual building work which has to be undertaken for such lofts is small. The loft is simply available or can be emptied for our hobby. In any event, we then have a space which is 'naturally' suitable for housing pigeons. Attics are, in general, dry. Heat rises. If the boiler is lit below the pigeons will benefit from it above. Moreover, the chimney runs up through many attics. As far as heat is concerned, therefore, we can get by without the provision which is sometimes necessary in other kinds of lofts.

Moreover, there will generally be a good amount of space available under the roof. And where there is space the pigeons will have air for a healthy existence. The fancier who does not immediately cram his space full of pigeons, on the basis of half a cubic metre per bird, will provide his feathered friends with the opportunity to expand their territory. Birds are very sensitive to this, even though it is a human concept. Attics often have the great advantage that one can build a loft in a loft, as it were. Roof lofts are generally less accessible than free-standing units. The owner or tenant who has outside access is fortunate. The fetching and carrying of accessories, food and baskets through the house often leaves its traces, even when done with care.

Opening for the pigeons to fly in and out and a window as a lookout post for the fancier.

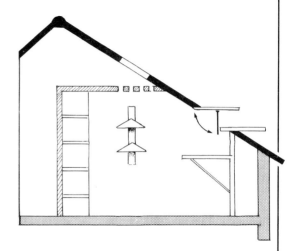

Section

If you have the choice, place the flying compartments on the sunny side. High attics need provision on the upper side to enable the fancier to catch his birds.

Light and ventilation from above, although no more than a lowered ceiling (left). Above, roof tiles with ventilation opening.

Ventilation

However large the area of living space in the attic, attention must be paid to ventilation. Ventilation will be bad, for example, if there is little direct communication with the outside air. If, moreover, the roof is lined with boarding this eliminates the 'breathing' of the tiles. An open ridge is the best solution for the ventilation problem and not only in roof lofts. In principle, a ventilator has no place in a pigeon loft but if the inflow of fresh air and its constituent oxygen is found to be really insufficient, a gently operating one can be installed, so placed and protected that it does not constitute any danger to the birds.

Characteristic

of a roof loft is its restfulness, which is the result of its elevated situation. Pigeon fanciers have found from experience that a move from below to above nearly always goes more smoothly than moving the loft from high up to near the ground.

These, too, are special roof tiles, intended this time for the cote system (see page 201).

Room loft

The structure of this kind of loft does not differ greatly from that of the roof loft, because the attic, in fact, is also a room. We are referring here to lofts in the ordinary rooms of a house. Sometimes, particularly in Belgium, whole storeys are used for keeping pigeons. Rooms can be very suitable for pigeons, but we must guard against the birds getting the upper hand. This can happen if they get the opportunity to loiter in the vicinity of the ceiling. It is essential, therefore, with a high-ceilinged room to insert a false ceiling. Rooms which are too large will have to be divided. In fact, the sport itself requires rooms to be split, e.g. into separate compartments for young birds, for widowers and for breeding birds.

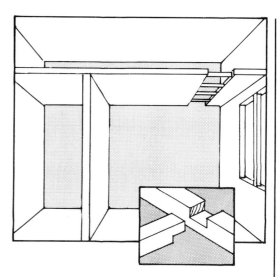

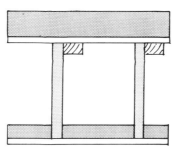

False ceiling
Rooms, particularly in older houses, are nearly always too high. They therefore have to be made suitable for habitation for pigeons by the installation of a false ceiling. The drawings show how this can be done.

In a shed

There are, of course, all shapes and sizes of sheds and sheds in all states of preservation. Depending upon these, work will have to be carried out as described in the section on 'garden lofts'. If the pigeons are kept in the roof of the shed, it is useful to refer back to what was said about roof lofts. Pigeons soon get used to the noise from other activities in the shed, although their rest periods must be respected. It is better to store strong-smelling materials, such as paint, away from the loft.

Garage loft

A loft in a garage may also be a good solution to the problem of housing racing pigeons. With the increase in the number of garages, both on new estates and as additions to older houses, the number of garage lofts has also increased. A garage loft is, in fact, comparable with a roof loft because the birds are nearly always accommodated over the garage. The great advantage is that such a loft is usually deliberately chosen, built and fitted with the necessary accessories. The garage space is often not used for storing a car.

Where it is so used, the division between the garage and the loft should be provided with an extra layer to keep exhaust fumes out of the loft. These fumes are harmful both to bird and Man.

In building the garage allowance must obviously be made for the weight of the additional floor, which is usually of concrete. The pigeons should not be allowed to come into direct contact with strongly smelling substances, such as paint and apples.

Cellar loft

If we recall the '4 Cs': chilliness, clamminess, cold and . . . cellar, we must immediately cross out a cellar loft. However, some devotees of the sport, who have no other means of accommodating their birds, rightly hold a different view. Cellar lofts are known from which good results have been obtained. They have therefore found solutions for such problems as admission of light, cold and, above all, air circulation. These may be special lamps, a modest number of birds and possibly a gently purring ventilator. So it is possible, but we must know our limitations and be on the lookout for artificial aids to compensate for the absence of the basic natural conditions.

Some fanciers have to make the most of the available space in order to be able to continue their hobby. Note the owner and the sputnik, which is level with his waist.

Balcony loft

Like the cellar lofts these lofts are also the consequence of extremely limited possibilities in the housing field. At the same time, they are often models of originality where it is a case of the owner making the best use of the means at his disposal.

Balcony lofts which, understandably, are found only sporadically, are generally very friendly clean places which are sometimes in intimate contact with the fancier's domestic life. He knows, of course, that he can keep only a couple of pigeons in the generally small space available. Their care costs little trouble; hence the cleanliness.

Aviary

Aviaries or runs, the places where the hens gather, are not just patches of ground separated off with wire netting. Small shallow aviaries, for example, facing west, southwest, northwest or north, are always bad. Still worse are small runs on wet ground not covered with tiles or other flooring material. Direct contact with clay, peat or sand often provides an ideal feeding ground for worms' eggs, oocysts etc. These conditions are not good for the birds' health. Obviously, the ground conditions can be so dry in some parts of the country that a reasonable subsoil can be created by putting down a 40-cm thick layer of coarse sand, which is regularly replaced. This may be the case on really well-drained sandy soils, for a high quality aviary requires a dry bottom. It is not provided with box perches, but with saddle perches. It should preferably not be too shallow and should be covered if it has the type of natural bottom described above. The situation should be such that the pigeons can sit out of the wind and be able to sunbathe for part of the day. Aviaries may be a simple resting place with just a few perches and other provision for resting, or they may be provided with such accessories as a long feeding trough, drinking and grit trays.

Small but good
An aviary need not and cannot always be large, but this need not mean that the birds cannot be very comfortable.

Steel structure
Some aviaries are built in the form of a steel cage. Side brackets or cross connections make it possible to fit perches for the birds.

Wire mesh

placed above the ground forms a very hygienic floor/foot bridge for an aviary. A simple plank can serve as a perch for the resting pigeons. (This is because pigeons do not have prehensile feet.) A concrete floor is also better than nothing, certainly if it is regularly hosed down.

More than four walls

After the erection of the four walls or putting up the necessary structures in the existing location, thought has to be given to choosing and installing the equipment for the pigeon loft. Whereas in building or making a conversion we may feel that we have to adhere to general standards for lofts, in fitting out we have a much greater choice. Moreover, the purchase of accessories is entirely dependent on the aim which we have in mind for our pigeons. In a breeding loft we need different things than in a loft for young birds.

There is a superfluity of equipment in the trade, good, bad and indifferent, depending on the supplier, accompanied by more or less relevant information. But in addition, quite a lot can be achieved with the use of our own skilled hands and those of our friends. It is certainly not a bad idea to take the advice of an experienced fancier. Your local racing pigeon association will certainly point you in the right direction. Lastly, always remember that concern for the wellbeing of the birds themselves again plays the most important part in determining the choice of accessories. In other words, function is the first requirement.

Heating

This time we shall look first at the human being in the loft. The sport of racing pigeons is for young and old alike. If it is at all possible, there should also be a little comfort in the loft for the latter category of fanciers and certainly for those who have a little more leisure and spend a considerable part of it among their pigeons. A thick sweater is a help, of course, and it is needed now and then, because it is not the intention to bring the temperature up to above 10–12°C on a winter's day. On the other hand, we must remember that

the birds can only benefit if their owner can spend his time calmly and unhurriedly among them, even when the weather is a little colder.

Pigeons themselves are not afraid of the cold. Wartime fliers were taken up into the air and were protected against the freezing cold only by their feathers, while their military attendants wore padded jackets and oxygen masks. In our climate, however, lower temperatures and damp go together. Dry cold, as during a severe frost, can do no harm, but damp cold is unhealthy.

Heat sources

Ancillary heating is necessary, particularly where the natural conditions are poor, such as where a minimum of light is admitted or we cannot stop rising damp. Lofts with flat roofs are soon found to need some artificial heating. Some improvement can be achieved through good insulation of the loft, including under the floor where the loft is built on the ground. Extra heat can be obtained by means of a drying lamp, an electric coil or an extension of the central heating.

Floor covering

The floor must be spotlessly clean, which means that it has to be thoroughly swept every day. Ill-fitting boards or unplaned and untreated wood soon become inviting breeding grounds for unwelcome guests. A floor which is even and as smooth as possible will prevent a lot of inconvenience and worse. An example would be birch plywood or other sheeting over a base of rough boards or concrete. This covering will also serve as a heat and sound insulator.

Where there is no time to sweep the loft every day, a layer of expanded clay grains, such as are used in plant containers, or lava, can be spread over the floor. Earth is quite unsuitable, although a layer of clean river sand may be spread over the floor, provided it is renewed regularly. We are somewhat hesitant to recommend this because not everyone finds it acceptable, and this is especially true where the subsoil is not bone dry. During the autumn and winter dried pea haulms may be used. Some lime may be sprinkled occasionally on wet patches. Damp makes lime hard, so seal your supply properly.

Forms of floor covering. Top, straw and (bottom) plywood, ideal for keeping clean.

Grid

Wire mesh makes an excellent floor covering not only in aviaries, but it can also prove a godsend in the loft itself for lazy fanciers or for those with limited leisure.

Perches

Perches play an important part in the life of the pigeon community. The pugnacious cocks fight each other for the best placed ones and will do anything to obtain a perch opposite their nest box. They will then make it clear to their fellows eyeing their prize that they should keep out of the way.

There are various types of perches: boards nailed at right angles to each other, simple wooden V-shaped perches and the same with a triangular piece of wood nailed across the front. There are also wooden box perches, but these have the disadvantage that hens can creep in them together and pay court to each other. The different types can be fixed to the walls individually, or in groups of three or more, but always close to each other. The bottom row must certainly not be fixed lower than about a metre above the floor. It is good to have as many perches as there are pigeons, as this avoids unnecessary fighting and disturbance in the loft.

If you study the illustrations alongside you will see that you do not have to be a skilled carpenter to make these perches. The compartment for young birds has space for a battery of a type of box perch with removable, downward pointing boards. These ensure that the droppings fall to the floor of the loft and are easy to keep clean.

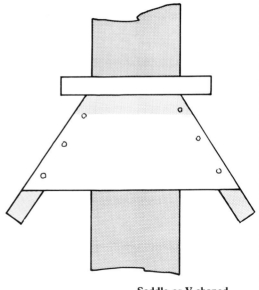

Saddle or V-shaped perch
with board nailed across the front – for cocks and hens.

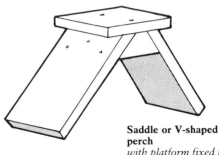

Saddle or V-shaped perch
with platform fixed to the top. Like all the other perches, this should preferably be made of wood or plywood.

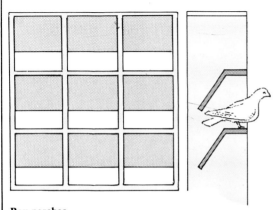

Box perches
with removable boards – for young birds.

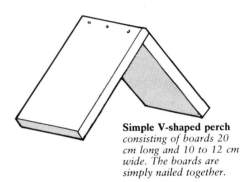

Simple V-shaped perch
consisting of boards 20 cm long and 10 to 12 cm wide. The boards are simply nailed together.

Perches in practice

Examples of perches in practice. The top photograph shows V-shaped perches in a loft for hens. The photograph left shows saddle perches with a board across and (on the right of the photograph) part of a battery of box perches.

Feeding troughs

One of the pigeon fancier's most important daily activities is the feeding of his birds. Old popular prints show pigeons pecking a grain out of their owner's hand. As we shall see in the next chapter, these scenes are still enacted today, although they have to be supplemented by pictures of birds feeding themselves. And they have always done so, of course. For this activity feeding troughs are recommended.

They can be supplied either open or with bars. The latter, although dearer, are to be recommended because there is much less wastage. The distance between the bars must be such that the smallest pigeon cannot get between them. The length of the trough depends on the number of birds feeding from it. Make sure that every bird is able to eat its share without having to push, thus causing great wastage. From this point of view, deep (ca. 25 cm) and rather wide troughs are the best. A good feeding trough is about 20 cm wide and has a hinged cover.

Feeding on the ground

The scattering of food on the ground is 'permissible' only if the fancier himself is present. It should always be done in small quantities which must all be eaten up.

Feeding tables

The main requirement for these is that they should be stable. They are placed under a landing board or trap, so that the pigeon can see the food and any of its fellows feeding when it returns from a race.

Feeding troughs

are available in all kinds and sizes in the trade. It is obviously also possible for the fancier to make one for himself. The dimensions are: 25 cm high, 20 cm deep and an average feeding length of 8 cm per bird. Deal or other timber can be used and galvanised iron for the bars.

Individual feeding

is something that should
continue to have a place in our
feeding system. It is good for the
fancier–pigeon relationship and,
hence, for the birds'
performance.

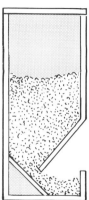

Automatic feeders
*It is even possible to use
mixing machines for
feeding where there are a
large number of birds.
They are filled with the
main constituents of the
feed which are then fed
through using the control
valves. The machines
must be so constructed
that they can be regularly
cleaned without too much
difficulty.*

Food storage

It is preferable to use solid, sealable drums, bins
or chests for storing food, or a modern, practical
aid such as a silo. Unsuitable materials, such as
jute or cardboard, only attract mice.

Grit containers
*The necessary grit,
crushed brick and other
materials the pigeon needs
are placed in strong
containers which will not
topple over under a bird's*
*weight. A good spot for
the containers is under the
nest boxes, if necessary, in
a larger container or
under a ledge.*

Two-in-one
*Glazed containers such as
this are suitable both for
holding water or solid
food for the pigeons.*

Drinkers

Modern drinkers are made of plastic. The earthenware and cast iron ones still exist. They are solidly made and difficult to keep clean. Anyone who still has to buy, would do best to make a choice from the wide range of lightly made and easily cleaned plastic models. They are provided with a variety of drinking openings, which should be positioned at the level of the bird's tail.

The correct place for drinkers is on a small, solidly built table, the top of which should be at a height of about half a metre above the floor. It is also possible, of course, to make a raised platform from two beams and a large piece of wood. In this way the water is protected from being polluted by droppings and dust. The area of the tabletop must be large enough for all the pigeons in the loft to take a drink.

Looking after the drinkers does not require a lot of time. They certainly do not need to be scrubbed every day. The main thing is to keep them free of droppings and to ensure that no dirt gets inside.

Water

is essential for the pigeons' life. Like most creatures, they would soon die without it. Ordinary mains water is adequate for assisting such vital functions as the movement of food and the formation of eggs.

Hygiene is assisted in the loft if the drinkers are regularly replaced by clean ones which have been dried by being inverted.

Pigeons can be given water in many ways. Some fanciers believe that their pigeons must be able to fend for themselves. They do not all find clean stopping places on the way home.

An attractive water trough on the outside of a breeding loft. As well as being attractive, it does not become polluted and is therefore hygienic, especially if a lot of birds have to drink there.

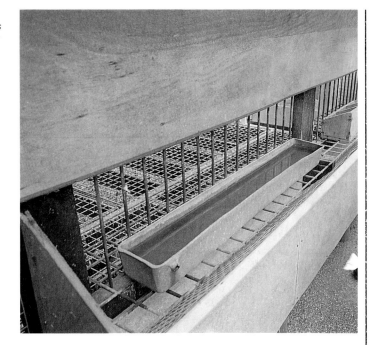

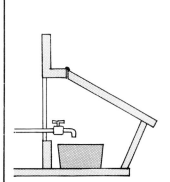

On a plinth

Pollution from dust and droppings can be avoided if the drinkers are placed high up (although obviously provision must be made for the young birds which are unable to fly!). Check that there are no sharp edges which can damage the breast feathers.

Cistern

to hold five litres of water. It is well protected against dirt and the birds can drink from it when they please.

Maintaining standards

Maintenance of a loft and its contents is a vital necessity, since our birds are not like common city pigeons who can make do with a little corner tucked away somewhere out of human reach. Because of their origins and the efforts demanded of them, trained racing pigeons are more vulnerable. Against this, however, if we look after them well and maintain the hygiene of the loft, they will retain their value for the maintenance of the species to an advanced age. This care forms a part of the daily routine, but a thorough

cleaning is needed at regular intervals to reduce the risks to a minimum. To use a weighty phrase, the policy should be prevention. In other words, to take measures to ensure the good health of the birds and to ensure their form and condition. Both are necessary conditions for participation in races.

The big clean-out

Twice a year you must make the effort to give the pigeons' living quarters a thorough cleaning. If you clean the various compartments housing the widowers, young birds and breeding birds every day, you will have less work than the fancier who is lazy in this regard. This does not mean that the less accessible parts of the loft will not sometimes be overlooked by even the most conscientious fancier.

However this may be, the floor, walls, food and drinking troughs, nest boxes and trays are scrubbed with water and disinfectant. The types and proportions of disinfectant are dealt with in the chapter on veterinary care. This is a good opportunity to take everything out, including food containers or whatever you use to store your supplies. Every nook and cranny must be cleaned,

so that parasites and the like do not get the chance to become a nuisance.

The big clean-outs are a good opportunity to carry out small repairs or improvements which make your life easier in the loft. Many fanciers combine the clean-out with the removal of the brooding compartments for the big moult (after the racing season) and their replacement for recoupling.

Pigeons are little disturbed by your cleaning and rebuilding frenzy. On the contrary, however much they are disturbed by sudden noises which they cannot place, they will watch their busy and trusted fancier with interest.

Whitewashing

Getting out the whitewash brush forms part of the routine of the six-monthly clean-out.
Non-powdered lime or whitewash is used on all the walls. The material helps to keep the loft dry, at least if the outside of the loft is also properly painted. Putty can be useful for filling cracks and holes. Floor white is available for use on the floor, although not everyone favours its use. It should certainly not be used to cover up a damp floor!

A burner

is a drastic instrument for ridding the loft of impurities. It can be useful, for example, after an epidemic. The burner must obviously be used with care to avoid starting a fire.

Disinfectant

We can spray the disinfectant of our choice with the trusty old spray gun. Many fanciers use a paint sprayer for this task (and obviously don't use it afterwards for its original purpose).

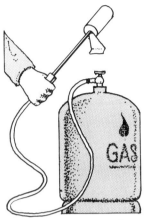

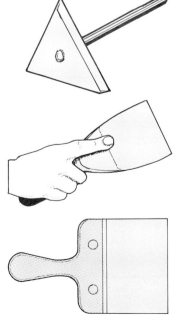

Materials

The cleaning materials should include a triangular scraper such as painters use, a broad flatting knife and a can.

Daily chores

We obviously do not have to take the expression 'daily chores' literally in every case. Although it is not unusual for the loft to be scraped clean twice a day, we are concerned here mainly with the attentive care of the pigeon fancier, with his eye for something out of place and – in his own interests – with regularity. It is not a question of a model loft, where everything is in its place, but of accessories not coated with droppings and a clean floor.

Bath

It is not strictly necessary for pigeons to take a bath, but it is certainly useful and the birds greatly enjoy it. This is not so much during the hot summer weather even as during or after a shower of rain. This is also true of birds in their natural state. If it is at all possible, therefore, ways must be found of providing the birds with this pleasure. Once a week, for example. No great engineering feats are needed for the purpose. A tray placed temporarily in the loft and a watering can will suffice, although it is of course possible to fit much more luxurious 'bathing installations', just as there are also LOFTS with capital letters and oversized bird cages.

Whatever provision is made, it is important that the birds should not be allowed to drink the bathwater. After the bath the water is covered with a greyish film and it may contain all kinds of impurities. Another important point, certainly in a small space, is to make as little mess as possible. We have already seen how important it is to have a dry loft. If the birds do not have the opportunity to bathe themselves, make sure that they all have a turn, including the most passive ones.

Slide-out tray permanently connected to the mains water supply.

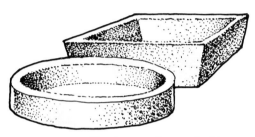

Simple trays for a refreshing pigeon bath.

Aviary bath

Once a week these pigeons in the aviary get a fresh bath. Adding some bath salts to the water provides the opportunity to clean the plumage and keep away such pests as ticks, lice etc.

The link with outside

A link on the grand scale. A landing platform for a large number of racing pigeons after a race or training.

The landing board is the vital link between the loft and the outside world. Pigeons drop onto the board after their training flights, but it is especially after races that a properly functioning link with the outside world can produce a gain of some seconds. It can ensure that the birds' nerves are not strained more than is strictly necessary. It is small wonder, therefore, that for several decades the greatest care has been devoted to this part of the loft, that new features are constantly being offered to fanciers and that the fanciers themselves invent the most ingenious structures to assist the birds in entering and leaving.

Requirements

As we shall see, the sport of racing pigeons has various techniques. For the present, it is sufficient to know that all the sections of a pigeon loft – if it has any – should have their own entrance. The latter must be wide enough to admit a number of birds at the same time. It should preferably be so placed that the fancier or members of his family do not keep bumping against projecting parts. If such a spot is not available, we shall have to restrict ourselves to a flight window or a demountable trapping board. The birds must be able to enter calmly and bad weather shouldn't be able to enter the loft.

A flight window

is the simplest form of entrance. The fancier simply sets it in the open position when the pigeons return home or if he wants them to fly. A flight window is, in fact, suitable for use only with the widowhood system.

The windows are open to enable the birds to be caught without delay after the flight.

Flap or board

The pigeon has much more difficulty in entering in situations such as in the photograph above, but once it is in it is in, whereas with an open flight window there is always the risk that it will fly out again.

Operating the trap

A proper means of closing the loft enables the fancier to decide whether the birds should fly or not. He can keep the loft open by some form of pressure mechanism – although from a study of the drawings this appears a somewhat exaggerated description – while the pigeon cannot escape once it is inside.

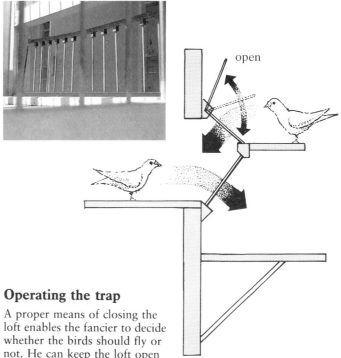

The trap can be set, as in the top part of the illustration, which means that the birds can get in but not out. It can also be bolted with a strip of wood, or it can be left open.

Sputnik

Where the space is available, a sputnik is an ideal solution to the problem of birds entering and leaving the loft. It has space both for the birds and their owner. The latter must not run the risk of bumping into the 'contraption'. The birds must find an unimpeded landing platform, particularly when they have found their way home after a race. This is also the moment when a well-placed sputnik, operated by a fancier who knows how to keep calm, can produce the greatest saving in time. There are all kinds of sputniks, some so large that the owner can even lean into them. It is an ideal place for racing pigeons to sunbathe. A closed sputnik is far preferable to a draughty open one.

Operating the sputnik

As with the trap, the sputnik is based on the principle of the pigeons being able to get in but not out. This comes into operation at the moment they have passed the bars, when they are easily caught. If the owner does this too brusquely he runs the risk of soon losing his 'cage with catching device' to his quick-witted birds.

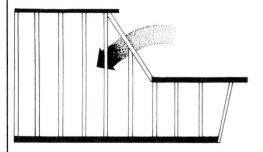

Diagram of how the sputnik works. The principle is the same as that of the trap.

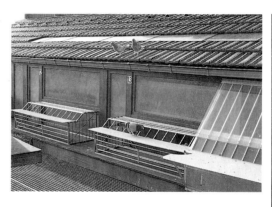

A bell
warns the fancier that one or more pigeons have arrived at the loft. The system is connected to the normal electricity supply and it can be so arranged that the bell can be fitted at the fancier's bedside, if desired.

An electronic eye
is another form of warning signal. It is the latest thing and not cheap to install. It comes into operation after the beam is broken by the pigeon.

The super-trap

is another device which, as the name clearly indicates, has been thought up with the aim of saving time. It comes from the United States and is specially intended for racing with young pigeons. The essence of the super-trap is the locking of the trap openings to prevent the bird entering the loft. The rubber ring is removed without the bird seeing what is happening. The young birds must obviously first be allowed to become familiar with the system before they are entered for races.

The two photographs give an impression of a super-trap: top, on the outside of the loft; bottom, on the inside.

Feeding

Feeding is one of the daily chores of
every fancier. Together with housing and
veterinary care it provides opportunities
for enjoying the sport of pigeon
fancying. Understanding this basic
aspect of the sport is essential for
successful birds

Feeding: source of energy

Living beings cannot survive without food. But athletes – and that is what racing pigeons are – make higher demands. Just as sportsmen also need a more balanced diet than those who run round the block once a fortnight. Moreover, racing pigeons are far more dependent on their trainers than their human counterparts. We must enable them to perform training work. To produce effort when it is really needed. But . . . racing pigeons do more than just fly: they breed, moult and 'hibernate'. All these activities demand a different approach to feeding from the fancier.

That approach must be aimed at enabling the pigeon to perform the vital function of the moment as well as possible. One function requires more energy or different building materials than another. The pigeon finds all this in the food package that we place before it. It is important, therefore, to know the composition of the package. In this way we can meet the needs of the season, of the activity concerned and so detailed attention is paid to this in this chapter. We cannot, of course, be continually racking our brains about the basis and effect of the birds' food, but it is useful to have some knowledge of it to refer to. It makes our work easier, as when we have to assess mixtures which are offered to us and it helps us to act correctly.

Composition of food

The pigeon's food is broken down in an ingenious interaction of its internal organs and made suitable for consumption. At the basis of this rich source are the so-called 'nutrients', of which there are three main groups: proteins, carbohydrates and fats. They contain 'elements', which are the building bricks for the body's growth, renewal and maintenance.

Carbohydrates, for example, consist of the elements of carbon, hydrogen and oxygen. These building bricks are in turn responsible for the manufacture of sugar, starch and cellulose, for example. The fats also consist

of three elements. The animal and vegetable proteins comprise a wide variety of building bricks. The pigeons themselves manufacture the animal proteins from the vegetable substances which we give them, so we do not have to 'assist' with animal proteins. Apart from the three main groups, another nutrient is rough fibre, to be found in the husks of barley, oats, beans and other products.

A healthy pigeon diet also contains such substances as minerals (lime, phosphorus, copper, iron and manganese), vitamins and trace elements (cobalt, iodine and fluor). The quantities are often minute, but no less important for that. All these nutrients can be found in the feeds, but one contains more fats, a second more proteins and a third more minerals. They also vary in the quality and quantity of each constituent. Variety is also important, therefore, from this standpoint.

Fads

A good regime has no place for fads. It is a matter of eating what the feeding bowl provides and it is the fancier who decides the content of the latter. He would do well, therefore, to give the less fancied ingredients first.

A varied, nutritious diet ensures a healthy flock of pigeons.

Vary the composition

The most important rule of our feeding policy is to vary the composition of the diet at every stage of the pigeon's life. Variation is indispensable even for resting pigeons, since different processes occur in every living organism. It makes no difference whether the organism is young or old, fully active or asleep.

Invisible to our eyes, for example, is the continual manufacture of skin cells, feathers and muscles. Equally invisible is the manner in which the pigeon's body is continually engaged in maintaining its temperature. These processes require a wide variety of raw materials. They can function at their optimum only if we apply variety to the diet.

The passage of food

Before considering the practical aspects of feeding, examining the various items of diet one at a time, we shall consider very briefly what happens to the food inside the pigeon's body. How digestion progresses. How excretion operates. And what practical lessons we can draw from these physiological processes or vital functions.

Everything that occurs between the beak and the cloaca, the excretory organ at the end of the rectum, has the purpose of breaking down the food into ever smaller fragments. Ultimately, even the large molecules are broken down. This is the point at which the blood is able to absorb the vital substances and transport them through the operation of the heart to the tissues where these substances are needed. They are partly used for one of the variety of activities which the organism of the pigeon is able to perform and partly stored as a reserve. Indigestible products are transformed into droppings, which form the start of a new cycle.

As we shall see, minerals and grit form important elements of the pigeon's diet. As always, we protect these items from unnecessary pollution.

Pigeons: equipped for vegetable matter

Pigeons pecking at grain are a familiar sight in the loft. But in the fields as well, if they get the chance, they busily search out what the earth has produced. Vegetable matter, therefore, constitutes the principal food source for our birds. Nevertheless, they will not scorn a slug, while earth itself forms part of their diet. All these ingredients of the food package follow a long path through the pigeon's body before the remains are expelled as droppings.

1. windpipe
2. gullet
3. thymus
4. crop
5. pectoral muscle
6. muscle from gullet to breastbone
7. thyroid gland
8. right carotid artery
9. right subclavian artery
10. left subclavian artery
11. right pulmonary artery
12. left pulmonary artery
13. lungs
14. heart
15. kidneys
16. liver
17. abdominal air sacs
18. pancreas
19. gizzard
20. first section of the small intestine
21. cloaca and anus

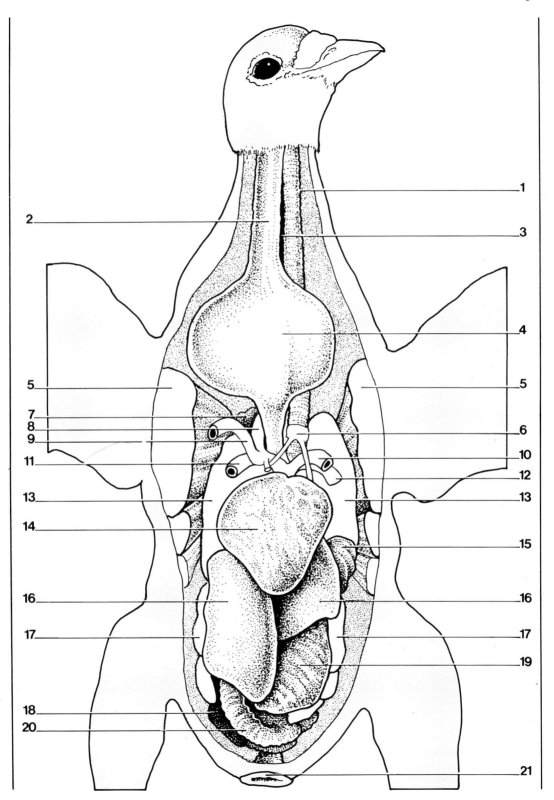

Digestion

There are only a few types of bird, of which the pigeon is one, which have a soft palate at the back of the throat. This is where the food which has been picked up begins its long journey through the body. The whole circuit is seven times as long as the pigeon itself. In comparison with mammals, for example, this is very short so the food must be easily digestible. The soft palate forces the largely vegetable matter, together with the saliva, into the gullet, at which point muscle contractions take over the pushing function of the soft palate, assisted by mucus from small glands.

The food then arrives in the crop. The duration of its stay there is determined by whether or not the intestines are full. After a short stay in the glandular stomach or proventricule – which is important for the splitting of the proteins – the food passes to the gizzard. If it is really quiet in the loft, you can hear the grit, driven by the gizzard, finely grinding up the food material. The grit performs the same task as our teeth. The gizzard passes the remnants of the food on to the intestine, where important transformations such as the manufacture of vitamins and the breakdown of sugars, fats and proteins, are performed by the pancreas, liver and other organs.

The digestive system

1. gullet
2. crop
3. glandular stomach
4. liver
5. spleen
6. gizzard
7. pancreas
8. small intestine
9. appendix
10. large intestine
11. cloaca

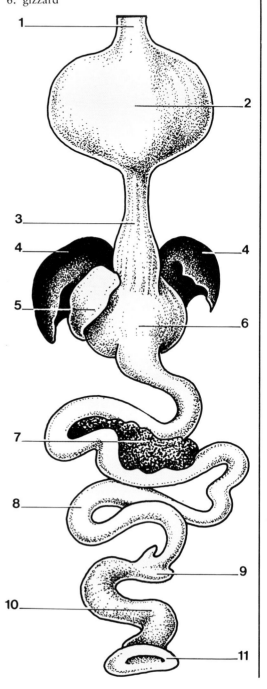

The gizzard

is the place where the food is ground up by grit. It has a thick lining on the inner side, composed of horny material.

Excretion

This is the disposal of the substances which the body is unable to use. Excretion takes place after the food has completed the whole journey through the digestive tract. The excreted substances contain practically no water. An increasing concentration of moisture occurs in the kidneys and cloaca. This is a very ingenious and complicated process in which the blood also plays a part, but what concerns us here is that it demands a fine balance between the various organs.

The fancier will become aware if this balance is disturbed when his pigeons are affected by diarrhoea. Disturbance can result, for example, from too rapid bowel movements, which may, in turn, result from lack of rest in the loft. The fancier must also take heed if his birds are abnormally thirsty.

The solid waste products are to be found in the droppings. As we shall see in the chapter on veterinary care, the droppings are an excellent indicator of the birds' state of health, not only for the vet but for ourselves.

Solid droppings, in the form of pellets, are a good sign. Wet droppings are, in any event, a sign to be on our guard. Droppings must be removed every day, since they are in the final analysis a chemical product. Left on the ground, they release poisonous gases, such as ammonia, and create a breeding ground for infections.

Young pigeons push their droppings over the edge of the nest bowl. Some fanciers remove the droppings more promptly than others.

Healthy droppings *are dry and fine in texture and leave no traces behind. The colour is determined by what the birds have eaten.*

Unhealthy droppings *are wet. It may not be necessary to take immediate action, but you should certainly be on your guard. Examine the droppings you find in the loft in the morning.*

Vitamins

The pigeon's body depends on vitamins for the supply of energy and the carrying of elements to maintain it. The whole metabolic process would also stagnate without vitamins. As the reader will know, the latter are designated by simple letters, but these letters stand for extremely important life substances ('vita' is Latin for 'life').

Top-class birds produce outstanding achievements. It is not surprising, therefore, that they are quicker to show a vitamin deficiency. Pigeon fanciers should therefore not hestitate to adopt the harmless practice of vitamin doping. They, in fact, do so every day when they fill the feeding trough with a varied menu. If the accommodation and care are also satisfactory and we make no excessive demands on our pigeons, extra vitamins will not be needed.

The situation is different where conditions are bad: where there are diseases which afflict the whole loft, where lofts have too little sunshine and too much damp. Under those circumstances extra vitamins may help. There are keen advocates of 'natural' vitamins, to be found, for example, in brown rice. Other people have no objection to giving factory-made products in the drinking water, even to birds who are going to participate in important races. Caution is advised here, however. Pills and potions must never take the place of a careful feeding policy in the loft or be allowed to cover up deficiencies in other departments of the sport.

Kinds of vitamins

Attempts are being made to replace the letters by which vitamins are designated by chemical designations, but it will be come time before we immediately recognise *ascorbic acid* as vitamin C. For completeness' sake in the following summary of the most important vitamins we give both the chemical and the 'old-fashioned' names.

A (*retinol*) Lack of vitamin A is said to cause eye disorders, conjunctivitis and inflammation of the cornea and mucous membrane, as well as greater susceptibility to pneumonia. A reduction in the secretion of hydrochloric acid, resulting in diarrhoea and the deposition of urine crystals in the joints, is also attributed to a deficiency of this vitamin. Extra vitamin A is given after a course of antibiotics. Yellow maize and peas have a high vitamin A content. Provitamin A (*carotene* group) is to be found in green vegetbles, carrots, fruit, cabbage, maize, green peas and linseed.

The B complex consists of more than ten types. Pigeons have a great need for vitamin B. It is abundantly present in such products as green vegetables, grain germs, green peas, unpolished rice, vegetable mould and yeast. Dull feathers, limpness and swaying are symptoms of a possible vitamin B deficiency. All types of the vitamin may be added directly to the water. This is done, for example, after a course of treatment with antibiotics. The best known members of the vitamin B complex are:
B1 (*thiamine*) in pulses and brown bread;
B2 (*riboflavine*) in grains;
B3 (*pyridoxine*) in pulses and meat.

Pre-germinated lentils (top) and soya beans.

Sprouts

Some pigeon fanciers who support a more natural way of keeping their birds favour feeding them germinated products. They start from the belief that sprouts are more nutritious in some respects than the products themselves. In particular they contain a higher proportion of natural vitamins, more minerals and trace elements and a higher proportion of sugar, which provides directly absorbable energy and easier digestibility.

The germination of (good quality) grains and pulses is carried out as follows: leave in a jar of water for one night at about 20°C (slowly germinating grain such as maize requires 24 hours, but oats require little more than one hour); rinse under the tap morning and evening to prevent rotting; continue rinsing when the sprouts appear. The sprouts are at their strongest after about three days. The sprouts which are not immediately needed may be stored for about a week in the refrigerator.

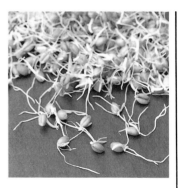

Pre-germinated wheat.

Salts

Fanciers who live near the sea will know that if their pigeons get the chance, they will peck up some salt from the beach. This does not appear to have any ill effects on their health. The birds who fly out to the fields also do this to maintain their salt reserve. Salt is essential for the vital functions. Creatures which eat vegetable products are particularly in need of it.

C (*ascorbic acid*), extremely important vitamin for Man and animal. The pigeon manufactures its own, mainly from green foodstuffs, although vets prescribe a supplementary dose after a serious illness. Besides being given in the water, it can be administered in the form of pills or injections.

D (*calciferol*) provides for the manufacture of lime and phosphorus, which are necessary for building up the skeleton. Sunlight is the main source. Three kinds of pulses in the mixtures provide for the manufacture of this vitamin. Cod liver pol contains a concentration of vitamins D and A. D3 is valuable as an extra pick-up after recovery from illnesses which have been treated with antibiotics.

E (*tocoferol*) is also called the fertility vitamin. Experienced fanciers give it to old pigeons who are apparently infertile. The dose is one drop of wheat germ oil in a pill of rolled bread crumbs. Peas, green vegetables and sprouted wheat grains contain the necessary vitamin E. It is also possible to give injections of vitamin E, together with part of the B complex.

We can administer vitamin E from wheatgerm oil by catching a drop in a couple of breadcrumbs rolled up to form a pill.

A summary of the pigeon's diet

Three groups of feedingstuffs are important for the pigeon's diet: cereals, pulses and seeds. The mixtures for the different vital functions, such as moulting, breeding and racing, are made up from these three groups. There is also a number of special products of widely varying character, from curly kale to garlic and from coffee to peanuts. Apart from their food value, they also have a certain emotional value which is not the same for every fancier. Although water cannot be called a true 'food' in every respect, it certainly has a place in this summary because of its important role in digestion. Lastly, attention is paid in this section on feedingstuffs to the use of pellets.

Buckwheat seeds on the plant.

Grains

A racing pigeon is first and foremost a grain eater. One can say that the bird has 'chosen' an excellent food from the nutritional point of view. Depending upon the species, grain has, in particular, a high content of starches, which are converted into glycogen (muscle sugar). As a result grains are excellent sources of energy for activities which make heavy demands on the muscles. Proteins and the minerals lime and phosphorus are represented in most grains in smaller quantities. The most important grains are maize, with a good value of 79.8, wheat (73.9) and barley (72).

One of the representatives of the grains which are so important for pigeons: barley.

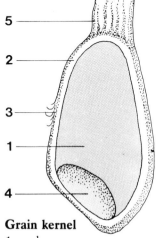

Grain kernel
1. endosperm
2. aleurone layer
3. bran
4. germ
5. beard

Pulses

Pigeon fanciers used to be rather lavish with these excellent protein producers and there are still some who include up to 60 per cent pulses in their mixtures. It is now known that this is too much of a good thing. Forty per cent is sufficient to guarantee that growth and renewal, the vital functions which depend on proteins, are properly allowed for. This proportion is also sufficient to ensure the proper formation of the young bird's skeleton. The minerals present in pulses play an important part in this process.

Experience has shown that stuffing the birds with protein-rich products such as pulses does not immediately produce bad racers, although research has demonstrated the link between excessively high proportions and wing diseases. The most important pulses include green and other peas, pigeon beans, lentils and vetches.

The green pea is undoubtedly the most important pulse. It is now known that excess, even of this excellent product, can do harm.

Seeds

Seeds form only a small proportion of the pigeon's diet, not more than a couple of grammes per meal. Seeds such as linseed, hemp, millet and sorghum serve another purpose apart from that of food. They are a much used means of furthering the understanding between the fancier and his birds, since pigeons find them very tasty. The fancier can therefore use the seeds to cement an attachment with the birds, to teach them to listen to his voice and to familiarize them with his gestures. For this reason seeds may be equated with sweets. Some extra seeds are given during the moult, particularly linseed and rape seed. Because of its aphrodisiac qualities, hemp is unsuitable at that time.

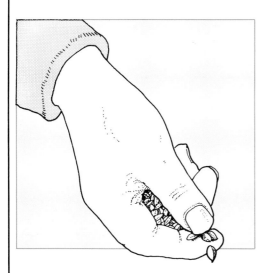

Weighing scales

An average meal for the adult pigeon weighs from 30 to 35 grammes. We mention this mainly for the sake of completeness. It is really not necessary to feed with an eye on the weighing scales, since it is not the intention to leave the birds to their own devices after filling the food trough. We look at how they eat and what they eat. From this and from the effect of the diet on their appearance and condition we drawn our conclusions for the sport. We also look at what food, if any, is left over and use it as a guide to changing the feeding pattern. All this is much more effective than a look at the scales. The latter only makes us nervous and may lead us to forget that it is better to look at the pigeons.

Maize

This grain is one of the standard elements of the pigeon's diet. It is a first-class product with many vitamins – A, B and E – although there are also a few provisos about its use. Despite its many good qualities, maize is an unbalanced food. It contains no building materials for the muscles and skeleton. It is primarily a manufacturer of fat and will be included in mixtures mainly when the birds are due to race or during frost. These are the circumstances when the existing fat reserves are being drawn upon. If these reserves are inadequate, the muscles themselves will be consumed. The unbalanced nature of the cereal is fully compensated by varying it with other foodstuffs.

A not unimportant advantage is that maize is relatively cheap in relation to its high feeding value and the pigeons readily eat it. The fancier must make sure that the grain he buys is healthy. He can judge this by looking at the gloss, the aroma and the soundness of the white germs. Today's abundance of maize in the livestock farming sector means that there is much less old, musty grain about than there used to be.

A great many varieties of maize are available and they go under various names. Gloss, fresh aroma and soundness of the white germs determine the quality of what we buy.

Yellow maize is the commonest sort. The pigeons prefer it to white or mixed and the provitamin A content is higher. If you have the choice, it is best to use more than one variety.

Anyone fortunate enough to own a piece of ground might consider growing maize himself, although in a climate like ours, which really has too little warmth, it will not be easy to grow ripe healthy maize. Proper drying – and this also applies to bought varieties – is very important. It prevents mould.

Wheat

Wheat contains a considerable number of proteins, the vitamins B and E as well as the substance phytase, which enables minerals to be released to the body. Pigeons love wheat, but they must not be given more than 15 per cent in their diet otherwise their digestion will be upset and they will lose their appetite. Moreover, great care must be taken with fresh wheat which can have a toxic effect resulting in diarrhoea.

A handful of wheat grains. A proportion of not more than 15% will be of benefit to the vitamin B and E economy and assist the varied composition of the diet.

Rye

Although rye was still recommended twenty years ago as an excellent cereal, opinions are now more divided. The rye itself, with its high content of carbohydrates and the presence of vitamins B and E has not changed of course, but some fanciers have suffered nasty experiences, probably as a result of feeding their birds too much rye. The birds concerned were mainly young pigeons whose digestion was upset and who had thick blood. Proportions of rye in the mixture in excess of 10 per cent caused red throats and blue flesh.

Apart from the fact that only a modest amount of research has been done into specific pigeon foods, the results of any research take some time to make themselves felt in everyday practice. So long as the relationship between the symptoms just described and the effect on them of rye has not been clearly demonstrated or disproved, it is advisable to be cautious. There are, in any event, enough other products at the fancier's disposal. Wheat, for example, can almost take the place of rye. The reader will only rarely find rye included in the mixtures discussed later in the chapter.

Barley

The special feature of barley is that we can use this grain to adjust the diet. More or less barley is added to the mixture according to what the pigeon is doing. For people who have little spare time this is an excellent way of giving the birds a correct feed. This cereal is rich in vitamins A, B, E and, particularly, D, is highly suitable for building a strong skeleton in young birds and promotes metabolism. The presence of husks makes the mash more porous, thus facilitating the action of the food juices and bacteria, thereby assisting the digestion. Moreover, good barley does not make the pigeons fat.

Barley is, incidentally, despite all its excellent qualities, not irreplaceable just as no food product is irreplaceable in principle. It is a question of knowing exactly what a product 'does', what its characteristics are and then looking for substitutes which do the same. In other words, we have to be well-informed about nutritional matters.

Barley is an exceptional feeding regulator and therefore very convenient for fanciers who have to devote attention to other matters.

Varieties of barley

Good barley is short, thick, heavy and dry. It is sound, yellow in colour and smells fresh, just as all grains must smell fresh. Aroma-less products have a bad name. There are short, heavy varieties which can be fed in larger quantity than the light, sharp varieties. Pigeons are certainly not mad about barley so if some is left over it is a warning that the quantity being given is probably on the high side.

Widows

without a cock will sometimes settle for each other when it comes to courting. These passions can result in infertile eggs. 'Widows' like this can be put out in the cold, at least if we have an aviary. But the laying of such 'useless' eggs can also be countered by feeding a little extra barley.

Oats

This cereal is easily digestible. It is richer than all the other cereals in protein and fibre and contains a considerable amount of fat. It is a source of vitamins B and E. All these characteristics make oats a first-class component of a varied diet, although we must be able to rely on the quality. Pale oats are not to be trusted in this respect.

There are unhusked and more expensive husked varieties. Both kinds can be used in the pigeons' feed, which may contain between 5 and 10 per cent oats. The choice of variety depends mainly on the proportion of husk in the weight. With some varieties the proportion of husk may reach 40 per cent. This percentage is rather high for the proper functioning of the bird's digestive organs. Lower proportions are found with black oats, which are not widely available, and with yellow, preferably pointed, oats.

Oats stimulate the sexual instinct. In contrast to fertilized eggs in the nesting dish, a fancier has no place for infertile eggs which are the result of mutual courting among the hens. Until the moment that the cock comes in view again after the race no oats should be fed to the hens in the run.

Sexual instinct

One of the characteristics of oats is that they stimulate the pigeon's sexual instinct. There are times when the fancier is not eager to have randy pigeons, for example, during the period that widows remain in the run. It is good to reduce the quantity of oats drastically at that time or to omit them altogether. There is no objection to the hens being sexually receptive when they return home. Parents with squeakers are also fed a minimum of this grain.

Raw feedingstuffs

product	protein	starch	rough fibre	fat
wheat	11.8	69.0	1.9	1.9
rye	9.6	69.5	1.9	1.7
barley	10.1	67.8	3.9	2.1
oats	11.9	58.2	10.3	4.8
maize	9.5	69.2	2.2	4.4
beans	23.5	48.5	7.1	1.5
peas	22.6	53.7	5.4	1.6
vetches	24.8	49.8	6.0	1.7
hemp seed	19.5	21.0	15.0	32.6
linseed	22.7	22.9	5.5	36.5
rape seed	20.0	18.0	5.9	45.0
sorghum	10.7	69.9	2.3	2.7
millet	11.6	56.1	9.7	4.3

Digestible matter

product	protein	starch	rough fibre	fat
wheat	9.7	63.5	0.9	1.2
rye	7.9	63.9	1.0	1.1
barley	7.4	62.4	1.3	1.9
oats	9.3	44.8	2.6	4.0
maize	7.1	65.7	1.3	3.9
beans	20.0	44.1	4.1	1.2
peas	19.4	44.1	2.5	1.0
vetches	21.6	45.8	3.9	1.5
hemp seed	14.6	19.0	?	29.3
linseed	19.3	18.3	1.8	34.7
rape seed	16.8	14.4	?	41.9
sorghum	7.8	56.8	?	2.1
millet	7.1	25.0	?	3.5

The summary above is intended to enable the reader to compare for himself the raw matter in the feedingstuffs with the digestibility of that matter. It is a guide towards making one's own mixtures, but one can obviously also consult the mixtures discussed later in the chapter for the various phases in the pigeon's life. One should always start with a good quality mixture.

Peas

The most important of the first series of pulses to be discussed here is the green pea. I is also the best possible pulse that we can give our pigeons. As far as the proportion of pulses in mixtures is concerned, a third, or 10 to 15 per cent, may consist of green peas. This proportion is justified by the rich content of vitamins B and E and the provitamin A. Proteins and minerals are well represented, although less so, for example, than in the representatives of the bean family. Moreover, pigeons have few problems with green peas, either actively, in picking them up, or passively, in digesting them. The price trend of this product is unfortunately not favourable, which must certainly be related to the large amount of labour required to harvest it. The fortunate owner of a vegetable garden – although the combination of vegetable growing with the equally time-consuming sport of pigeon racing is an unlikely one – can do something about this himself. He will not have to be satisfied with the insipidly coloured peas which are sometimes offered in trade mixtures.

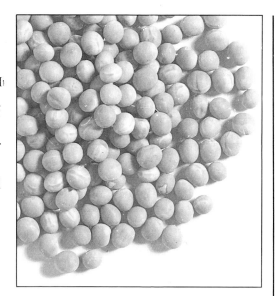

Other peas

Besides the irreplaceable green pea the pulses include: numerous other peas, some of them with melodious names, Tasmanian, Chinese, grey and sweet, but also the brown and common marrowfat. The latter is also the only one in the range which approaches the green pea as a source of vitamins. Except that . . . pigeons are less enthusiastic about eating this tough somewhat larger green pea. As always, this mainly imported pea must be fresh.

Beans

There is a whole range of beans with names which differ from country to country and region to region, and some of which are also eaten by Man. They include brown, white, speckled, scarlet runner, horse, sheep, field and . . . pigeon beans. As far as food value is concerned, the product to which the pigeon has given its name is not the bean *par excellence* for our feathered friends. The name was prompted much more by the ideal size of this pulse for pigeon consumption. Some of the beans just referred to are indeed very large. All beans are heavy food, which means that the proportion included in the mixture should not exceed five per cent. This is enough to enable our

birds to benefit from the rich content of proteins and minerals. The vitamin content is modest. If he adds too many beans to the mixture, the fancier has to contend with the disorders characteristic of the time when fanciers still prized this product too highly: thick blood and inflammation.

Fresh beans must be the watchword. We can check this for ourselves. Old beans are dark or even black. If we bite into them, it can break a tooth because they are so hard. If you don't dare risk this, suspect beans can be put into some damp earth. If they are young beans, they will germinate after a few days.

Vetches

This pulse is expensive, but we do not need to include very much in the mixture. Four or five per cent will suffice to enable us to benefit from the good qualities of vetches: they contain many proteins (actually the ideal of all pulses – not more than about 30 per cent) and many minerals. The grain size is very suitable for consumption by racing pigeons and the birds are very fond of them. But the fancier should note that vetches stimulate the sexual urge.

The colour of the different varieties ranges from light to dark blue. The grains are rather perishable, but can be given to the birds again after being washed and dried in the sun.

Wild vetches
can also be found, although increasingly less plentifully. They grow at the sides of banks and ditches and on other, mainly sandy, soils. They also decorate some wild gardens. The quantity present there is probably too small to supply sufficient material for the pigeon's daily meal.

Lentils

Like vetches, lentils are among the most expensive of the pulses included in the mixture, so that they are included in only some of the mixtures offered for sale. There are all kinds of lentils, varying in colour and size, the latter being partly determined by where the crop is grown. Although pigeons are fond of these pulses, which have a food value comparable with that of peas, they must not make up more than a few per cent of the total ration.

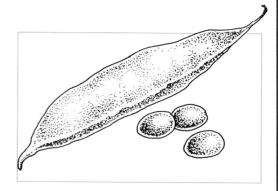

Katjang idju

The appeal of the katjang idju is the result of effective advertising rather than the true value of this product for the pigeon's diet. The katjang is certainly not comparable with the green pea, as is sometimes suggested. It has a reasonable protein and vitamin B content but much less provitamin A. Moreover, it is quite an expensive product. The katjang is not a bad pulse, but it adds nothing to the familiar and cheaper range of pulses.

Lupins

Lupin seeds may be added in a modest proportion to the pigeon's dish. They consist mainly of proteins, fat and minerals. We are referring here to the sweet lupin, the other species are poisonous.

Seeds

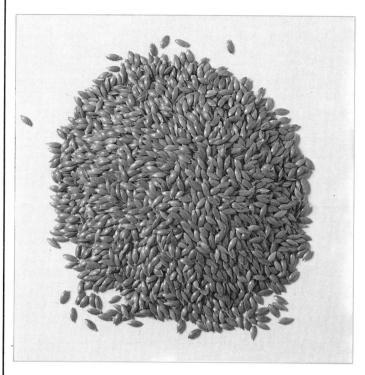

Canary seed

This pigeon delicacy has many names. The reference to 'delicacy' indicates that care must be taken in feeding canary seed. It is a good way of gaining the birds' trust, but if we are too generous with it we spoil them for other foods. If we bear this in mind, there is no objection to giving all the pigeons this seed, which resembles short, glossy oats, but is much more nutritious, on every day of the year, but it will be expensive.

Paddy

This unpolished form of rice has a favourable effect on the vitamin supply, provided the proportion remains between two and four per cent of the mixture. The main vitamin present is vitamin B.

Hemp

This seed is certainly as good a means of gaining the pigeons's trust as canary seed and is just as much loved by the birds. An attentive fancier will therefore certainly make use of this protein-rich and sexually stimulating product. It is a successful dessert particularly during the pairing season and during races. Feed a small handful to the widowers and a pinch to the squeakers in the nest bowl.

Hemp.

Linseed

The existence of linseed oil is already an indication that linseed is a product rich in oil. In addition to fats, the favourable effect of which on growth and health is strengthened by the presence of unsaturated fatty acids, it contains the necessary proteins. Linseed has a laxative effect because it encourages the mucins and should therefore be given only in modest quantities. Another reason for feeding only moderate quantities is that the concentration of linseed may result in the formation of poisonous hydrogen cyanide. It is generally accepted that linseed has a favourable effect on the moult and encourages the formation of soft plumage.

Rape seed.

Rape seed
Cole seed
Wild mustard seed

These three kinds of seed also contain a good proportion of fats and protein. The aphrodisiac effect, which is well-known to experienced fanciers, derives from the mustard oil present in the seeds. The seeds must therefore be given with discretion. They may be fed during the pairing season, for example, and to young birds and widowers, but not to widows. The winter is a less appropriate season for spoiling the birds — and these seeds do spoil them.

Sorghum
Kaffir corn

This seed is useful when the birds are being put into their baskets. A couple in the mixture is enough. It is not very rich in nutrients. The poorer qualities contain a high proportion of rough fibre.

Sunflower seeds.

Sunflower seeds

Sunflower seeds are the product of the tall and stately sunflower plant. They enrich the pigeon's body with several proteins and minerals and with a lot of fat and rough fibre. It is preferable to feed the smaller varieties with a strong husk. The pigeon's droppings may assume a purple colour as a result of eating black or striped seeds, but this should not cause any concern.

Safflower
Indian sunflower

These are different names for the same plant. They are often mentioned in mixtures, but if you have the choice it is better to use the native sunflower which is richer in minerals but otherwise has the same composition.

Buckwheat

Although this triangular seed is regularly listed in mixtures, it is poor in nutrients and is really included to give greater variety.

Millet
Sorghum

The food value of these two seeds is comparable with that of wheat. The different varieties can vary considerably in size and colour. There is no reason to use millet and sorghum instead of other seeds.

Buckwheat.

Pellets

The value of pellets is governed mainly by the trust we can place in the manufacturer. Trust it is, because you cannot tell from the outside of this pressed meal food what it contains. You are therefore dependent on the proven quality of a particular brand. You must be able to rely upon the constant use of first-class food sources, upon the pellets being free of disease and upon them containing ingredients not to be found in ordinary mixtures, such as coconut, carrot meal, grass meal etc. Provided they fulfil these conditions, pellets can make up 20 per cent of the total diet.

When they were introduced in the 1930s and '40s, and long afterwards, pellets were regarded with suspicion. Fanciers who used them were not true pigeon fanciers . . . But from the beginning there were also well-known fanciers who used them as supplementary feed and sometimes even gave them as a full feed.

Initially, feeding experts were wary because pellet suppliers made it appear as though they had an answer to all feeding problems, while even today there is still so much to be investigated in the area of feeding. This critical approach was therefore certainly not just a result of wishing to kick the manufacturers where it hurt. The study of 'old' handbooks written by authoritative pigeon experts will show how much has been added to knowledge in this field, so that some caution is recommended, even in 1986.

No single mixture, no single standard feed and hence no single pellet, no matter how carefully made up, can guarantee success. The same mixture, the same standard feed, the same pellets are given by champions and by fanciers who never manage to gain a certificate.

The 'prohibition on pellets' has long been superseded. Provided they are given with discretion – but this is true of all foods – they are a useful addition to the diet.

Vitaminized pellets

One of the latest developments, originating in Belgium, is the inclusion of the so-called 'vitaminized pellet' in the mixture. This combination is intended as a complete diet, including vitamin shots. The pellets contain nutrients in appropriate doses: vitamin A, the complete B complex and D, E and K; amino acids, the building blocks for the formation of proteins, such minerals as calcium, phosphorus, sodium and fluor in appropriate quantities and the trace elements iron, zinc, copper and iodine. This again is not a miracle food nor a sure guarantee of first prizes, but it can spare the fancier a lot of headaches and reduce the use of all kinds of preparations.

Menu of the day

Armed with some information about the effects of food and the food value of a large number of products, we can now consider the composition of the day's menu, the menu for breeding birds, young parents, racers, moulting birds and resting pigeons. What follows are suggestions; carefully selected, but cautious averages. How you vary them is a question of trying things out, of observing what your own pigeons will take, of literally feeling how the birds react to the feed. A somewhat nervous stock makes different demands from a loft full of quiet birds. But a nervous fancier, or one who has many other things to do, will deal differently with the daily menu than someone who is able to spend a lot of time with his birds. What is important — and this applies not only to feeding — is that we must not overestimate our possibilities. There are fanciers who succeed in giving the same feed on every day of the year. They vary only the quantity and ... the birds' achievements. But insiders know how difficult this is and how much time it takes.

Breeding mixtures

With breeding we are concerned with the different stages of the cycle and the need at every stage to attend to the needs of both the parents and the offspring. The pigeon milk, which also plays such an important role at this time, is dealt with in the next chapter, on 'Breeding'.

Breeding begins with pairing. It is good, therefore, at the initial stage, before the pairs are brought together, to adjust the feed to stimulate the mating urge. A useful feed at that time will include 25 per cent pulses, mainly peas, beans and vetches, and a couple of grammes of fine seeds per pigeon per day. Of the seeds a half will consist of rape seed and hemp. The mixture may well comprise a total of twelve to fifteen different ingredients. During the mating period we have to feed our pigeons when it suits them. They are busy with other things and sometimes miss the regular mealtime. After the eggs have been laid we become rather more strict and reduce the quantity of food somewhat. Because of their aphrodisiac effect, rape seed and hemp should no longer be given. The guideline now is at least 30 per cent barley and not more than 20 per cent pulses.

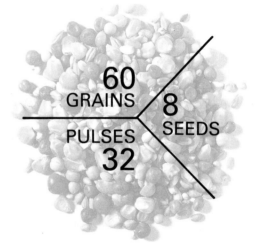

Composition

The breeding mixture proper:
grains 60% (maize 32%, three varieties; wheat 15%; barley 10%; husked oats 3%)
pulses 32% (green peas 12%; English peas 4%; brown peas 5%; beans 6%; vetches 3%; lentils 2%)
seeds 8% (sorghum 4%; sunflower seeds 2%; paddy 2%).

The breeding mixture proper appears on the menu from the moment that the young broods are about four days old. It must be rich in various proteins, contain a lot of vitamins and a lot of minerals. When the squeakers are three weeks old, we can add some pellets and linseed and canary seed.

Mixture for young pigeons

As with the breeding mixture, we are not giving just a snapshot and describing the appropriate food for that moment. We begin with the food to be given in the first few days after weaning, i.e. at an age of from three to four weeks. At that stage we can make do with the breeding mixture described on the previous page, but with the 'full dish'. Some extra peas, beans and maize will certainly encourage the young ones in learning to eat. This means that they can feed at any time of the day. After about a week they have to become accustomed to our regime. Part of this consists of set mealtimes, twice a day.

At this stage we stop giving them the breeding mixture. This moment coincides with when the birds begin to fly. The second stage lasts until the birds are through their first moult. The mixture given may be supplemented with good quality pellets and some fine seeds. (Not too much hemp and rape seed.) It is a good idea from the training point of view to feed this treat from our hands.

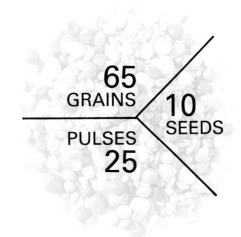

65 GRAINS

10 SEEDS

PULSES 25

Composition

Mixture for young pigeons, to be used until immediately after the moult. Participation in races should make no difference:
grains 65% (barley 20%; wheat 10%; maize, three varieties, 25%; unhusked oats 10%)

pulses 25% (green peas 10%; beans 5%; vetches 3%; English and brown peas 5%; lentils 2%)
seeds 1;% (sunflower 2%; paddy 2%; sorghum 4%; buckwheat 1%; safflower 1%)

There are fanciers who, wishing to 'not make dainty seed pickers of them', give their young birds an exactly calculated diet from the second day after weaning. Others see no objection to giving them a full bowl for a week, i.e. to having food always available. Others again allow the birds to become accustomed as soon as possible to the large grains and pulses which are so important. Thus no strict rules apply. The most important thing is to adopt a careful approach and adapt the regime to our own experience.

Racing mixture

When we come to deal with the sport itself we shall discuss in detail the various types of race and the interest in them. For a proper understanding of the aspects of feeding associated with racing, we mention at this point that, apart from training flights, we shall be concerned with short-, medium- and long-distance races. There are more or less specific pigeons for each type of race. But the feed must also be adjusted to the distance to be covered.

Sprint races can be flown on the breeding mixture. With races of between 300 and 500 miles it can do no harm to give a little more feed than usual for a few days before departure, certainly if heavy going is expected. For distances above 500

miles it is a good idea to place a small dish with mainly maize and wheat in the brooding compartment for four days before the birds are put in the baskets and to fill the dish with a fresh mixture every evening. It is striking that many pigeons scarcely peck at this little extra treat on the final day.

If the birds' performance fall off markedly after a few flights, consider starving them for a short time and then giving them a reduced diet after a few days. Continue with this until the birds are thriving again.

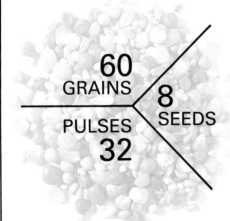

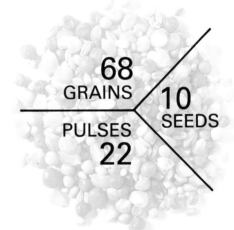

Composition (short distance)

(*same as breeding mixture*)

The breeding mixture contains sufficient natural reserve for distances up to about 300 km: *grains 60%* (maize 32%; three varieties; wheat 15%; barley 10%; husked oats 3%)

pulses 32% (green peas 12%; English peas 4%; brown peas 5%; beans 6%; vetches 3%; lentils 2%)
seeds 8% (sorghum 4%; sunflower seeds 2%; paddy 2%).

Composition (long distance)

grains 68% (three varieties of maize 40%; wheat 13%; barley 10%; oats 5%)
pulses 22% (green peas 10%; beans 3%; vetches 3%; brown peas 3%; English peas 2%; lentils 1%)
seeds 10% (sorghum 3%; sunflower or

safflower seeds 3%; paddy 4%).
Top up with a little fine seed each day, 50% of which should be rape seed and hemp.

Travel fat and body fat

Tougher races demand more reserves, which are to be found in fat. One cannot go on feeding fatty products with impunity; once the limit has been reached they are converted into body fat. It will be clear that all this extra weight will have to be carried, so this is not the time to throw our feeding discipline overboard and stuff the birds with food for fear that they will have too little reserves. On the other hand, the principle of minimal feeding can be dropped when the birds have a flight of over 500 kilometres ahead of them. If there are both racers and stock birds in the loft the fliers may be fed in the nesting compartments.

Stock birds

Pigeons who do not take part in the racing and – valuable – breeding birds who must stay behind for other reasons are fed only barley in some lofts. A rather more varied diet, however, with 40% barley, 25% maize, 15% wheat, 10% oats and 10% sorghum, for example, need not cause any problems, provided it is fed sparingly.

Hopper system

With this system the birds may eat as much as they want at any time. Success is possible with this way of feeding only if the pigeons are allowed to become accustomed to it and the birds who gain too much weight are weeded out.

Moulting mixture

Translated into feeding terms, moulting means drawing upon the renewal capacity of nutrients. Or, in practice, on the proteins and minerals of linseed, for example. If they possess a good general constitution, which can be achieved through constant attention to proper feeding, even if no wing feathers fall the pigeons will certainly suffer no additional problems at this time. The new feathers will also be dry and hard. The number of ingredients is, if possible, even more important during the period of the moult. You can safely start from a minimum of ten, even if your supplier says you can make do with less.

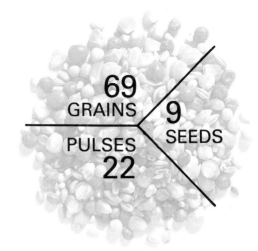

69 GRAINS
9 SEEDS
PULSES 22

Composition

Grains 69% (maize 30%, three varieties; barley 20%; wheat 13%; unhusked oats 5%; rye 1%)
pulses 22% (green peas 10%; beans 5%; vetches 2%; brown and yellow peas 3%;

lentils 2%)
seeds 9% (sorghum 4%; paddy 2%; sunflower seeds 2%; buckwheat 1%). (A minumum of 4% linseed and cole seed in any event.)

Winter mixture

In judging the nature of the mixture to be given during the quiet winter period, account must be taken of the kind of accommodation and the warmth it provides. The varying winters in our part of the world, in combination with sheltered or open quarters, can give rise to considerable differences between one loft and another. The watchword, especially during the winter, is: be sparing. But where there is extreme cold, for whatever reason, the birds will benefit from a little extra maize, since maize helps to keep up the body temperature. At the same time, the total quantity of food can be increased somewhat. If the temperature rises above freezing point, we return to our sparing regime (be sparing, but feed consistently twice daily). This is the best way to prepare for a new cycle of feeding and racing.

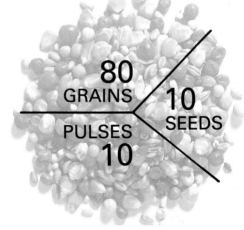

80 GRAINS
10 SEEDS
PULSES 10

Composition

Grains 80% (barley 45%; maize, three varieties 20%; wheat 10%; unhusked oats 5%)
pulses 10% (green peas 5%; English and

brown peas 4%; vetches 1%)
seeds 10% (sorghum 5%; paddy 2%; sunflower seeds 2%; buckwheat 1%).

The greens challenge

Whoever has had the opportunity to watch free racing pigeons, even if only for a couple of hours, will know that greens exert an irresistible attraction on these birds. The true fancier knows that this attraction is stronger than usual when there are young birds in the nest. The feeding experts have not yet discovered what the value is of this pecking at the grass, but neither have they found any disadvantages. We may have our own ideas about this greens challenge, provided our own birds do not succumb to it.

Fielding

Anyone who has had the opportunity to watch his own or another fancier's pigeons away from home will have seen that they do not readily miss the chance to pick grain from the fields. This urge has nothing to do with poor treatment at home, with being given too little to eat or being fed the wrong mixture. Our pigeons evidently find the pickings elsewhere to be at least as tasty as what is served to them in their own loft.

In deliberately allowing the birds to visit the fields fanciers are taking the risk that they will come into contact with harmful pesticides, but these same fanciers also know that pigeons find endlessly varied diets there. The real problem is how this risk can be avoided for the whole population of the loft, even if one has misgivings, when one lives close to farmland.

Carrots

One sometimes sees rabbit keepers dragging home sackfuls of the dandelions of which their animals are so fond. Some pigeon fanciers would also like to 'go foraging'. Admittedly, one is often asked about it, but there are easier alternatives. One of these is the carrot, the large winter variety, which has good keeping qualities and so can be used over a long period. Horse carrot also comes into this category. If a small area of the garden is set aside for this crop, one has to take only a couple of steps to provide one's bird with a delicacy. Diced carrot is an excellent food supplement for the winter and greatly enjoyed by the pigeons.

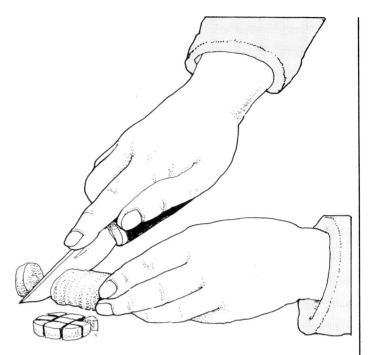

Curly kale

You may safely put it to the test. Your pigeons will leave almost nothing of a stalk of curly kale hung up in the loft on a winter's day, certainly not if they have had some time to become accustomed to it.

Yet more green alternatives

Carrots and curly kale are only two ways of meeting the need for green food in an urban loft. We mention a few here in order to stimulate your imagination: parsley, lamb's lettuce, ordinary (not hothouse) lettuce, chickweed, finely chopping stinging or dead nettle, assorted weeds with chopped grass etc.

Supplementing the feed bin

Besides the ingredients in the feed bin there is a long list of products which form part of the feeding package. One is more necessary than another. Personal habits, traditions passed on from father to son and all kinds of factors play a part. One fancier smiles at the stubbornness with which a fellow fancier swears by cheese, while he himself calls his favourite pigeon the peanut king. What is certain is that no objection can be made to ways of gaining the attachment of the birds, provided the means are not harmful. None of the products discussed in the last part of this chapter are harmful. We are not referring here, incidentally, to the indispensable contents of the grit bowl and the drinker.

Grit

As well as water, grit must always be put out for our pigeons. Neither is put out for its food value, but grit and water supply the basic conditions for the proper functioning of the digestive process. We have already seen in the discussion on the passages of the food through the pigeon's body that the purpose of digestion is to break down the food into increasingly smaller particles so that it can ultimately be absorbed into the blood. In contrast to mammals, birds do not have teeth with which to carry out the initial coarse grinding. The function of the teeth is taken over by grit, which performs its extremely useful task in the gizzard.

This also explains why ground shells alone are of little value to pigeons. They are digested far too quickly to enable them to carry out their grinding function properly. To the layman it seems strange to put stones in front of the birds . . . but the birds pick them up themselves somewhere if they get the opportunity and we do not supply them. It is striking how hens, when they are due to lay, do their best to take in shells, sand and whatever other coarse matter they can find.

Wear

The interplay between the gizzard and the grit is so close that the grit eventually wears out, even with healthy birds. An infection in the intestines further accelerates this wear. The fancier who always has good grit and red brick set out in the loft is automatically helping the invalids.

A good grit mixture

consists partly of gravel, brick chippings, various kinds of broken shells, charcoal and lime. It is sometimes said that grit and brick chippings are necessary for the production of strong egg shells. However important this aspect may be, there is sufficient lime in healthy fodder for the production of excellent egg shells.

Brick chippings.

Minerals

Lime, magnesium, phosphorus, iron, salts and sulphur are the minerals which are indispensable for pigeons. We have already seen with salts (page 105) that the quantities concerned are very small, but nevertheless important. We can provide our pigeons with minerals and vitamins simultaneously if we give them some chicken food.

The vital element of water

Water deserves a far more important heading than 'miscellaneous'. It is a vital necessity for the pigeon, as is clearly indicated by the functions it performs, of which we list only the most important: transport of the food, formation of digestive juices, transport of waste matter, egg formation. The point we wish to make, of course, is that water is so common. We have only to turn on the tap. Apart from emphasizing the vital function of this liquid, there is little to add.

Providing water

How do we supply our pigeons with this essential liquid? The two extremes of ice cold and standing for hours in the summer sun must be avoided. In other words, a happy medium, not a refrigerator and not a stove. Fresh water is good, but we need not overdo this. Pigeons are not delicate. Excessively fastidious fanciers would be panic-striken if they knew how their birds quenched their thirst en route, drinking in gutters and stagnant, brackish water. Nor do drinkers have to be cleaned and polished two or three times a day. The main thing is to avoid scale forming and to refill the container when the water becomes dirty.

Purification with garlic

The purifying action of garlic is well known. There is consequently an increasing number of fancier who swear by adding a crushed clove of garlic and the skin of the clove to the drinking water at regular intervals.

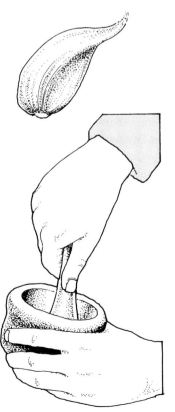

Garden mould

Investigation of the digestive tract to ascertain the causes of death has repeatedly shown that pigeons are real soil peckers. (The soil was incidentally not the cause of death that was being investigated.) This is also clear from the birds who sometimes persistently work over a lawn. If you want to be kind to your birds, particularly parents feeding their young, put out a tray of garden mould. Eating this can do no harm.

Feeding

The art of feeding is to let the pigeons eat what is good for them. They must therefore be hungry. This is achieved by feeding them sparingly and by adhering to a rigid schedule of two meals a day. During the rest period one meal a day will suffice. If the pigeons start going over to the drinkers or rummaging in the feeding trough, it is high time to stop feeding.

Delicacies

We have saved the treats for the end. And that is how it should be. Birds who eat up all their food may have a little extra. In contrast to children, we cannot forbid pigeons to beg (even if it helps with children). But of course we do not deny the bird if 'our' ration has already disappeared into its raised beak. And to maintain the comparison with children a little longer, we may not punish pigeons by witholding from them the delicacy which they always receive at a more or less set time.

For example, when they have irritated us by coming in at their own time. By doing so we only make things worse. The creatures remember and make things even more difficult for us the next time.

Under the category of delicacies we include such things as bread, cheese, peanuts, acorns and other treats exclusive to some lofts.

Bread

Pigeons are 'sold' on bread. They apparently find it even more delicious than the wheat from which it is made. It is preferable, however, not to stop feeding this grain because bread has a lower food value, but it is not so bad that we cannot use it to gain the birds' affection. Wholemeal bread is preferable. The same remarks apply to rusks.

Peanuts

Whereas bread and cheese are out-and-out luxuries, the peanut contains so many nutrients that the remains from your party can be consigned to the pigeon loft without any objection. This will provide the birds with a lot of protein and fat and a by no means negligible portion of minerals and vitamins (from the B complex). Whether they are shelled or unshelled, the pigeons will have to grow used to them. They will liven up limp birds. Peanuts are also increasingly being used as a means of creating the necessary fat reserve for taxing long-distance races.

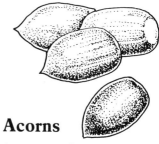

Cheese

There is no harm in feeding pigeons some cheese by hand, even though they do not really need it with the average nutritious menu. Nor are they particularly fond of it, although they learn to appreciate it.

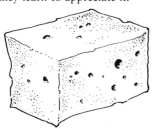

Soya

Soya is one of the constituents of pellets but may also be given to the birds separately. The soya bean contains high-value proteins which are little inferior to animal protein. This product is also becoming increasingly valued.

Acorns

Acorns contain so many nutrients – their composition is similar to that of maize – that they could even form up to a third of the winter ration. They can be collected free in the open, so if you have the energy to collect sackfuls of them, you can save on your budget. When you bring them home the acorns should be spread out and kept dry, either in the open air or in a cool place indoors, in order to prevent mould.

Breeding

With breeding we are at the beginning of the pigeon's life. Here each individual fancier makes his contribution to the evolution from the rock pigeon to the champions of today and tomorrow.

Buying, breeding or . . . acquiring

Although nearly every fancier devotes himself to breeding, beginners will obviously have to start their hobby with pigeons from someone else. This will not be difficult. Every true fancier is pleased when a newcomer arrives to strengthen the ranks of the club. The new member soon receives excellent offers from fellow members in the form of eggs or birds, all of them free. This is an encouraging start, certainly if the newcomer's budget is limited.

Another way is to ask an experienced fancier for guidance in obtaining a few specimens from him. There is the possibility of purchasing from well-known lofts, but that may prove expensive. There are also pigeon markets and public auctions.

The most sensible thing to do is to start with a few young pigeons which we can allow to become accustomed to *our* environment and *our* way of managing them. It is estimated that 95 per cent of pigeons move in this manner, free or in exchange, from loft to loft! If you make proper inquiries beforehand and take into account the origin of the newcomers, this will get your hobby off to an excellent start.

Pigeon markets

Many fanciers visit the pigeon market. These visits are usually intended mainly as an outing, but they often result in the purchase of a few young pigeons. Those who race young birds and do not have sufficient pairs of older birds, may be lucky here at relatively little cost, but assessing the health of the birds can bring its problems.

Conditions

One of the first requirements is that the pigeons we acquire should be in tip-top health; otherwise we bring disease into the loft and our acquisition is doomed to failure before we start. If you feel you are unable to gauge the health of the birds, call in the help of a more experienced colleague.

Sales

There are lofts where the demand for pigeons is much greater than the supply. Well-known fanciers, in particular, understandably do not wish to be approached every day by unknown prospective buyers. In this kind of situation use is made of a public sale or auction. Pigeons are also sold at an auction in the event of a death or a fancier retiring from the sport or moving away.

Which ???

If an old hand at the sport allows us to choose from a batch of young pigeons, the right choice is up to us. The annoying thing, however, is that there are no specific criteria, assuming they are all healthy birds. You can let your feelings decide; observe which birds look alert, which have retired into the background, but these are not true criteria on which to build. The best thing perhaps is to ask the owner for help. He knows his pigeons. Moreover, the majority will give the prospective buyer a bird with which he can achieve results, rather than one about which there are question marks. Quick but nervous racers will do less justice to themselves with a somewhat nervous fancier than with a colleague blessed with nerves of steel.

Heredity

A handbook should discuss all aspects of the hobby, so this means it has to deal with a lot of topics, both practical and – where this is necessary for a better understanding of the practice – theoretical. The subject matter is not easy but it is extremely useful background material, even for those fanciers who seem to have an inborn feeling for matters of heredity, since nobody can succeed without a little luck, instinct and routine. It would be all too 'easy' if we could win every time on the basis of its principles. Heredity is, fortunately, not a simple addition sum with only one answer. If it were, all the excitement would disappear and only the best of the class would carry home the honours!

We can obviously only give basic information here, but there are a number of well-documented books, both about the laws of heredity in general and their application to racing pigeons, in particular.

Quality and quantity

Chemical substances, known as *genes*, determine the inherited characteristics of living creatures. They are therefore also called 'units of heredity'. These units are to be found in large numbers in the *chromosomes*, small threads in the nucleus of a cell. Inherited characteristics are divided into two groups: qualitative and quantitative.

Qualitative characteristics are determined by a single gene. To understand how those characteristics operate we still refer to the researches and the conclusions of Mendel, the Austrian monk who lived in the second half of the last century. *Mendel's Law* states that certain characteristics are dominant, i.e. they suppress other characteristics. The colour red suppresses blue, for example; in other words, red is dominant. The suppressed blue is said to be *recessive*. If a pair of chromosomes has identical genes for a particular characteristic, they are called *homozygotic*, i.e. purebred. If the genes are not identical, the chromosomes are *heterozygotic*. What this means for us in practical terms is that two blue pigeons can never produce a chequered offspring, so do not let anyone tell you otherwise,

even if the vendor is not deliberately trying to deceive you.

Quantitative characteristics are determined by a number of genes. We distinguish between characteristics which are determined by only a small number of genes, such as endurance and shape characteristics, and qualities such as ingenuity, speed and suitability for a particular distance, which are determined by many genes. With crossing these characteristics are inherited *recessively*, i.e. they are working towards an average. The pigeons acquired for a particular crossing, therefore, should be selected carefully.

Mendel's Law in practice

Recessive inheritance

Chequered colouring, which occurs both with the red factor (red, red-chequered and grey) and the black factor (black, chequered and blue) is inherited recessively. A pure chequer × a blue will produce an impure chequer in the first generation. Reversion in the second generation gives the following result per four pigeons (a more detailed account would give higher numbers, the following is only an example): one pure chequer, two impure chequers and one blue.

The picture in the third generation would be: pure chequer × blue = impure chequer; impure chequer × impure chequer = one pure chequer, two impure chequer and one blue (out of four);
blue × blue = 100% blue.

As has already been indicated, two blues never produce a chequer, even with chequered ancestors, since blue pigeons no longer have the chequered factor in their heredity.

Dominant inheritance

Red is dominant over black. Because of the dominance of red, pairing of a pure red factor cock with a black factor hen produces only red factor offspring, both cocks and hens.

Mother and daughter

Alongside we see illustrations of a female (top) and her daughter who have produced outstanding results, both in racing and breeding. Although they are of different colours, they were bred in pretty close relationship.

Rule of thumb

No immediate improvement of the breed is achieved by inbreeding, although it is possible to 'fix' the characteristics which are present in the breed. It should be noted that this includes the bad as well as the good characteristics. Only if the fancier possesses outstanding birds to begin with, which are resistant to them, is inbreeding the way to proceed. Crossing can have positive results if it takes place with a bird of at least equal quality. Crossing has an excellent effect on vitality, especially if it involves two separately inbred racers.

Heredity in practice

Without losing sight of the theory, we examine in the following pages ways of building up the best possible population of our lofts. Methods are cited and various examples given, but without a sharp eye and the recording of data about our birds, it will be difficult to improve our loft through our own breeding.

Selection

In order to be able to continue winning every year and to avoid our loft becoming congested, we have inevitably to select from our flock. Moreover, we are also aiming to obtain a model pigeon, a type that suits us and that we would like to see. This also demands 'culling' of specimens which depart too far from the norm.

The beginner will soon hear it said that the basket is the best selector, by which experienced colleagues mean that he must examine his birds critically and choose on the basis of their performance which pigeons to keep and which have to be 'sifted'. (What is being discussed here, therefore, is not natural wastage.) The same colleagues will certainly wish to be helpful in making the choice, just as the club is there to help with word and, where necessary, deed, in the responsible killing of the birds.

Beautiful *and* good

Selection purely on the basis of external characteristics can produce truly beautiful, ideal racing pigeons conforming to the standard type. In selecting in this way no regard is paid to such characteristics as character, homing ability, flying speed etc. The result is the creation of the show bird, which gives many fanciers a lot of enjoyment during the winter months. Crossing of this type with good fliers gives the chance of beautiful birds which are also formidable racing competitors. The Olympiade shows at the international level pigeons combine racing achievements with beauty.

Racing or breeding

If we base our selection on racing performance or breeding value we generally pay much less regard to outward appearance. The pigeon does not then need to have a beautiful round head or an extra broad back. The placing in the race or the breeding results determine the bird's sporting value. Nevertheless, certain external characteristics, such as good wings, soft plumage and supple muscles, remain desirable even with this form of selection.

Pedigree formation

It has already been suggested in the introduction that the racing pigeon is most probably descended from the rock dove. The same *Columba livia*, as it is known scientifically, is the ancestor of many pigeon lines. There are reasons to assume that it was deliberately bred in one way or another since time immemorial. In this way, the varieties which were raced in Belgium at the beginning of the last century shared other external and internal characteristics with their distant ancestors.

The present competition pigeon has its origins in those early years of the 19th century. It is a crossing of the Liège pigeon (black, small, short beak, frill, dark eyes) with the Antwerp (crossing of tumblers, smerles and small croppers). This does not mean that there is not a tremendous variation within the line and fanciers are still adding new varieties, for the dream of most fanciers is to be able to create a homogeneous, championship-winning line of their own. This can be achieved only through a planned and painstaking approach, the use of inbreeding and/or the crossing of good lines. This demands good administration in which the parentage is literally an open book. Once you have achieved a particular pedigree it is easier to obtain results, since pigeons of similar descent all require roughly the same care. This causes fewer headaches and provides fewer opportunities of making mistakes. The form needed for a race is also reached more quickly with a team of this kind.

Grandfather and grandson

Grandfather (above) and grandson possess not only a striking similarity of outward appearance, but are also each other's equals in the winning of prizes.

Crossing

The majority of fanciers pair their birds on the basis of crossing, thereby bringing together many inheritance factors of dissimilar origin. The offspring will bear little or no resemblance to each other, neither in external appearance nor in the characteristics needed to make a good racing pigeon.

The advantage of crossing is that we can enhance the quality of a particular characteristic, at least if it is present in the crossing 'material'. Well-planned pairings made in this way increase the vitality of the loft.

Line breeding

The starting point is two pedigree pigeons of outstanding quality which are balanced with each other in type. The most pleasing, best developed and strongest offspring of this pair are needed for the next season. The pedigree cock is paired with his daughter and the pedigree hen with her son. In the following year the best young hen is paired with the pedigree cock and the best young cock with the pedigree hen. We can continue in this manner until the vitality begins to diminish. In the meantime the offspring are fully tested in the sport to see whether the results match expectations. Proved specimens are suitable for mutual pairing from the second generation.

The Janssen pigeon is a typical example of an inbred race and a good example also of how the theories of inbreeding and line breeding can be carried out in practice. Crossing of a Janssen pigeon with another pigeon from a good inbred strain of competition pigeons has ensured successes in many lofts by raising vitality.

Cousins

This cock (top) and hen are cousins. Because they belong to a good strain and are good racing birds, there is a reasonable chance of obtaining valuable offspring from such a pair.

Free pairing

In contrast to the so-called reasoned pairing through crossing and inbreeding there is free pairing, which means that the pigeons choose their own partners. Some advocates of this method do not have a very high opinion of the results of reasoned pairing. Nevertheless, some of them also vary their practice, for example, by first allowing what they regard as the best cock and the best hen to have first choice and then the lesser gods. Fanciers sometimes also select exclusively from the racing loft for free pairing. They hope then that the urge to return home will be increased because the pigeons have selected a partner of their own choice.

Inbreeding

By inbreeding is meant breeding with blood relations. Theoretically, therefore, it involves the pairing of specimens with identical genes, resulting eventually in a large number of homozygotic pigeons, i.e. pigeons who form only one type of cell with the same gene. If the result is a sum of good qualities, we have achieved our aim, but we must take care to ensure that suppressed characteristics do not sneak into our inbred race. This would mean that, by this breeding method, we were also establishing the bad qualities in the birds' heredity. The widely expressed opinion that inbreeding is equivalent to degeneration does not apply, at least if a strict selection is constantly applied. If the stock declines it can be revitalised by means of a good cross.

Breeding scheme

Some inbreeding pairings:
father × daughter
mother × son
grandfather × granddaughter
grandmother × grandson
brother × sister
Very common pairings:
uncle × niece
aunt × nephew
cousin × cousin

This inbred hen (top) and cock have been bred from a grandmother × grandson. As crossing material with a partner from another, good, inbred strain, they have a good chance of producing offspring of tremendous vitality. This method has often proved successful, certainly as a way of breeding new champion racers.

Pedigree card

A useful aid in breed creation is the careful completion of the pedigree cards, but a modern aid such as the home or personal computer has also proved its value to some fanciers.

About birth

We are now finally leaving the theoretical aspects of the preparations for a new life, although practice was also kept firmly in mind in the foregoing. We now deal in chronological order with the various interesting steps from the minute cell to the new brood and the fancier's place and decisions during that couple of weeks.

Timing of breeding

The purpose of breeding largely determines when the activities in this sphere begin. Someone who wishes to excel with young pigeons would want to pair as early as possible. This will enable him to race young birds which he can treat in the same way as their older fellows. If the aim, however, is to achieve good results with old birds, particularly over the longest distances, the owner will subordinate the pairing to the sport. He then chooses a time which allows his fliers to leave at the right state of the nest, including a plumage which allows championship performance. The race programme can also be a factor in determining the breeding date. In Belgium the races for young pigeons begin as early as May, while in the Netherlands they usually do not start until early July.

The Associations in both countries (Belgium and the Netherlands) do not issue the permanent registration rings, the pigeons' passports, until 1st January. This means that the squeakers may not be older than seven days, if we at least still wish to ring them responsibly. Working back, this gives the mating date of 37 days before 1 January: 7 + 18 (brooding days from laying of first egg) + 12 days from mating to egg laying). Mating should not really take place before 25 November. A pigeon may sometimes lay freely in the winter when the weather is mild and there is adequate light.

Preparations for breeding

The pigeons must be ready to mate. The fancier achieves this by gradually switching healthy birds from their winter diet to a heavier mixture with less barley, supplemented by some fine seeds. Healthy also means a check of the droppings and of some of the pigeons by the vet. Together with the help of natural or artificial light and heating, the conditions have now been created for a successful breeding season. The card index, the exercise book or the computer will again be provided with data.

If it clicks between the partners all our preparations, at least up to this moment, will not have been in vain.

2 February

Many pigeons were and are paired on 2 February (Candlemas), particularly by fanciers who practise the widowhood system (see 'The sport'). The birds lay their eggs on about 14 February and on 5 March there are squeakers in the nest bowl. When the latter are about 22 days old, the hen will have laid again. After ten days of incubation the eggs are removed and the sexes are separated, or the cocks are put into widowhood.

Pairing and driving

Cocks and hens which are ready to breed are the ones which quickly reach an understanding with each other when they are put together. They both show clearly what they want from one another. They caress each other with their beaks and soon afterwards the hen crouches and pushes her vent feathers aside. The cock then mounts her and presses the lips of his anus against hers. At the same time he ejects a large quantity of semen which enters the hen's oviduct on its way to a ripe ovum. The birds then want to rest. They caress each other as they lie in the nest bowl, but are soon ready for a fresh mating.

It is important that the pair should learn their way to their nesting box as soon as possible, because this is when the period of pursuit begins, with the cock driving the hen. One may say without exaggeration that he cannot be kept away from her. Some cocks go so far that the fancier is forced to lock them up. They must be given food, water and grit of course.

It occasionally happens that two birds which it has been planned to mate want absolutely nothing to do with each other. In such cases the fancier has to intervene and find new partners.

Nest building

As soon as the pigeons have found a place to build their nest, a lot of to-ing and fro-ing begins. All kinds of materials can be used to satisfy this urge: wing feathers, twigs, pieces of barbed wire, string, plastic and a whole lot more. Nevertheless, pigeons give the appearance of being very particular. Every likely nest-building item is first inspected with the beak before they decide whether to carry it to the nest. The fancier can give a helping hand by making available tobacco stalks, long pine needles (from the common pine) and/or straw.

Pigeons collect anything that will make a nest to their liking.

Nesting materials

The most suitable nest-building materials are tobacco stalks, pine needles, straw, ready-made nest-mats and anything else which the birds themselves collect. Hay is not suitable: it goes mouldy and the birds' legs may become entangled in it, so that the whole nest is turned upside down.

Tower building

Pairs of pigeons occasionally erect gigantic constructions compared with which this nest is only modest. However much we may admire their energy, it is sensible to intervene if the nest grows too high, because the function of the nest is to provide a safe home for the eggs and young. With skyscrapers there is a good chance that something may go wrong when the birds enter or leave the nest. Moreover, youngsters which fall out of the nest may be seriously injured or even killed.

Tobacco stalks.

Long pine needles, from the common pine, to serve as nesting material.

Old newspapers, changed every day, or a piece of corrugated cardboard, with some lime if desired, help keep the nest hygienic.

In the bowl

A well-built nest in a suitable bowl means a peaceful nesting box and rest is one of the conditions for a successful breeding season.

Is everything in order?

The whole interior of the loft must already be in good order when pairing and driving begin. The nesting boxes must be in position, the nest bowls clean and sufficient nest-building material available. It is a good idea to provide the cocks with a nest box about a fortnight before mating to prevent later fighting over territory. Moreover, old birds should be shut up in their familiar nest boxes and the yearlings given a choice from the remainder. Otherwise old cocks might lay claim to two boxes. Sending in the 'manager' avoid misery later!

Nest bowls

Nest bowls of all shapes and sizes are available in the trade, but not all are equally suitable. We prefer to see sturdily made stoneware bowls, quite broad, with high rims and with large ventilation holes (1). In particular, the bowl must not be too flat (2 and 3) and not be completely rounded on the inside (4), because otherwise the nesting material will move around too much. Disposable nest bowls of papier mâché are available (5). Some fanciers make their own boxes with a mesh bottom, but these are not suitable for the widowhood system. It is advisable to place an old newspaper or a piece of corrugated cardboard under the bowl during the breeding season, perhaps with a thin layer of lime. This can be changed daily and assists hygiene.

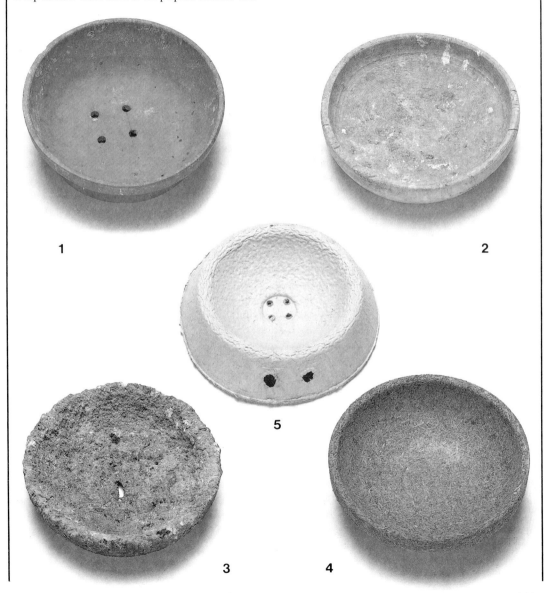

1

2

5

3

4

Egg laying

The first egg is usually laid no longer than eight or nine days after mating. Some hens lay quickly, others take a little longer. Normally speaking, a healthy hen should have laid within 14 days. With late young hens we have to make allowances in this respect. If a hen still has not laid eggs after a fortnight, there must be something wrong with her health, with her egg-laying mechanism or with the love relationship with the partner. It is then a good idea to place some pot eggs under the hen, so that incubation is not delayed for too long. Where the relationship with the cock is a cool one, the fancier should have intervened sooner. Sometimes a short period of separation helps. Where the hen is egg-bound it is important to call in the vet as soon as possible. The vet can give medicines to stimulate or ease laying. Warmth is also a means of relieving hens in this condition.

The first egg is always laid towards evening; the second egg over one-and-a-half days later in the early afternoon.

This is the moment it was all about: the moment when the eye tooth has pecked a hole in the shell. But before this stage is reached tense days lie ahead, certainly if it is the first time.

Fertilization must have occurred between 24 and 44 hours before laying. The actual incubation process does not begin until after the arrival of the second egg. Hens only protect the first egg against cooling down too rapidly.

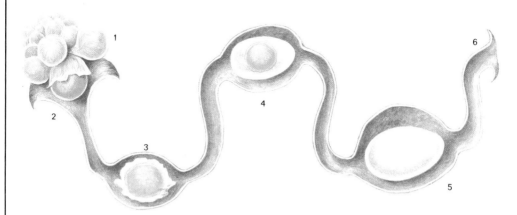

Development of an egg

The ovary with incompletely developed yolk follicles and nearly ripe yolks still in the membrane (1). Ripe yolk with ruptured membrane descending into the oviduct (2). In the first section of the oviduct albumen is deposited round the yolk through movements of the oviduct (3). The central section of the oviduct, the uterus, containing the complete shell-less egg (4). The egg passage or vagina (5) with the complete egg, which leaves the body via the cloaca (6).

Hatching

Under normal circumstances the end of incubation may be expected about 17 days after the laying of the second egg, but it may take a day longer if the eggs have been left unprotected for any length of time.

Incubation

As was just mentioned, actual incubation does not begin until after the laying of the second egg. Both the hen and the cock share in warming and protecting the eggs. The cock sits from about ten o'clock in the morning until five o'clock in the afternoon and the hen sits for the rest of the time.

A freshly laid egg is white with longitudinal light and dark stripes. Blood on an egg, which may occur with young hens, should not cause us concern. It should be left in the nest and not cleaned.

Growth in a fertilized egg takes place under the influence of heat and moisture. No human intervention is needed; in fact,

human intervention does more harm than good. The birds also carry out the necessary regular turning of the eggs themselves, with their beaks.

Fertilized or infertile?

After about five days you can see whether the mating has had the desired result. If the egg is held against the lamplight the spider-shaped embryo can be seen. Fertilized eggs begin to turn a bluish colour after incubating for ten days. Infertile eggs retain their pure colour from the beginning. After the tenth day the egg becomes opaque except for the air cell. The end of incubation is in sight when the young bird has made its first contact with the outside world by pecking through the shell.

Food supply

There is no objection to brooding pigeons putting on a little weight, but they must not become lethargic. The quantity of food is accordingly reduced at this time. Finally, incubation with food within beak reach makes little demand on the birds. The proportion of barley, in particular, is reduced, but the variety of the mixture is maintained. The pairs are given food in the trough on the floor so that the fancier can see how much they eat. Brooding pigeons grow very handsome, as can be seen from the photograph. They become as smooth as eels.

A pigeon's egg after incubation for three days. No real development is yet observable.

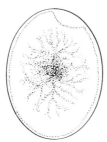

The spider-shaped embryo becomes visible on about the sixth day.

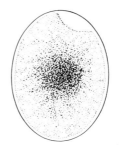

Development proceeds rapidly. On the ninth day the egg has already almost ceased to be transparent.

From the eleventh day, even to the practised eye, only the air cell is still visible.

144

First days of life

During birth the most active role is played by the chick itself. After chipping at the shell, it is the young cock or hen which breaks its way out of the egg. The parents assume full responsibility for the care of the young, including food supply (p. 150). The fancier is only a spectator as far as this is concerned, although he does ensure that the parent birds are properly fed.

Newly-hatched squeakers, as the very young pigeons are called, nearly double their weight during the first few days. After 20 days they are already some 400 grammes heavier. After about 14 days the fancier takes over the care of the young birds from the parents. He feeds them the breeding mixture described in the last chapter.

Egg tooth

The squeaker chips at the shell with its egg tooth as a preparation to freeing itself. The egg tooth appears in the photograph above as a white dot at the end of the beak.

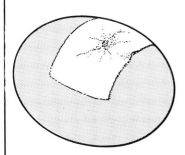

Damage

The embryo will generally die if the egg is accidentally damaged, but if the membrane has not been torn, sticking a piece of blotting paper over the crack in the shell may sometimes save the life inside.

The final straws

Birth takes place without any haste. 15 or 20 hours may elapse between the chipping and the actual emergence of the new-born chick. Anyone wishing to be present at the birth would be advised to take an extra day off because there is no firm guide. Even among experienced fanciers there are those who have seldom or never been present at the exact moment of birth. As we wait, the chick rotates on its axis, making dents on the inside of the shell. When it has completed the circuit the top falls off the shell and the chick works its way out with one of its legs. Birth has taken place. The young bird is apparently helpless, wet and blind, but this soon changes.

Twins and triplets and sex

A pigeon egg occasionally contains two yolks. If fertilization occurs a twin may be born. We refer to a triplet where a hen lays three eggs in a single cycle.

In general there is a match between the build of the hen and the shape of the egg. Long hens, for example, seldom lay very round eggs. That you can predict the sex from the shape of the egg is nonsense, of course. Hens who lay short or round eggs do not only have daughters and long specimens do not bear only cocks. Nor does the position of the air cell tell us anything about the quality or the sex.

Dimensions

Racing pigeon hens do not all produce the same size eggs. By way of exception, a mammoth egg is sometimes laid, about the size of a bantam hen's egg. It will come as no surprise to learn that laying it involves a great struggle for the hen. Incidentally, if the laying lasts too long, the germ cell will nearly always have died. Many fanciers prefer the larger eggs, although we do not of course mean the giant-sized eggs just mentioned. Smaller eggs often come from the first clutch of a young hen. It is sometimes said that small eggs point to a lack of vitality. Eggs without a smooth shell often do not hatch. The grainy texture is the result of drying out, which is fatal for the germ cell.

Misshapen eggs
may well rouse our suspicions. Are we right to let them develop? Curiosities usually do not make the best contribution to the sport.

These parents are taking good care of their offspring. They radiate pride. They look at the photographer with an expression of 'don't try to disturb the peace here'.

In the bowl

Two squeakers in the bowl is best. They warm each other and the rubbing against each other stimulates the breaking of the quills. Healthy squeakers grow apace. In general, they have to lie still; only at feeding time do they make themselves heard. Afterwards peace returns and the food they have received gets the chance to be properly digested.

Natural selection

Although it demands much effort, the majority of squeakers will emerge healthy and well from the egg after some hours. A few have considerably more trouble. The membrane is too tough, the chick pecks holes instead of dents or the chipping is not done in a circle. In such cases we can help by tapping the circle in gently with a finger nail or by removing the top of the egg. Never remove the chick itself from the egg. This is fatal. You can indeed question whether it is not better to let nature do the work. Weak specimens fail to survive and this may be regarded as a form of natural selection.

Navel

About seven days after birth the fancier should inspect the squeakers in the bowl. He should check whether they feel 'tender'. The flesh must be pink, the navel retracted and not inflamed. Nor should any hard yellow pellets have formed.

Rings

Champions and scrubbers – they all wear a ring. The little aluminium cylinder covered with a layer of hard plastic, together with the owner's certificate, distinguishes each registered racing pigeon from its fellows. Some pigeons have a name, given to them at birth or after an impressive performance. But there are also a great many ring numbers which a lot of fanciers mention with respect. The pigeons have to become acquainted very early with the ring. It is best not to wait longer than seven days before putting it on. Apart from registration – without the ring the pigeon does not officially exist – it also serves as a means of identification, even though a good fancier has no difficulty in recognising his own birds.

Dutch ring, 1985

Belgian ring, 1985

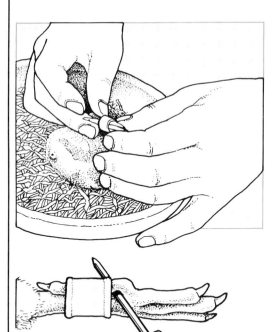

Ringing

Hold the three front toes and first push the ring over them and then over the hind toe, which is extended back. Draw the hind toe carefully through the ring. If the leg is very fat, a little soap will help to ease on the ring. The hind toe can be pulled through gently with the aid of a small nail, for example.

The ring

Permanent rings are issued each year with the accompanying ownership certificates. The owner should check that the numbers on the ring and the certificate agree. In addition to the foot rings there are the rubber rings worn during races. We shall return to these in the next chapter. The foot ring is made of aluminium and is protected by a layer of plastic. In order to increase identifiability, the plastic coating is given a different colour each year and different colours are used by different countries. The letters used are abbreviations of the country of origin.

Care

The care of the old birds bringing up a nest of young demands special feeding. The food must contain a richly varied assortment of proteins as well as many vitamins and minerals. Also do not forget to make fresh grit, brick chippings, pitchstone, good black earth, mineral mixtures and animal protein available to the birds. As soon as the parents start giving hard grain to the two youngsters, the fancier must provide a bowl with some extra food. The bowl must be nearly empty by the next mealtime. With only one young bird in the nest this precaution is less essential.

Droppings check

Apart from being a passing phenomenon of the transition to solid food, watery droppings may be a sign of an outbreak of sickness. Investigation by a vet can establish this.

If a young bird is clearly backward in developing, do not hesitate to remove it. You should obviously distinguish between a squeaker which is having problems in development from a brother or sister which hatched a day later.

Healthy droppings

Young pigeons who produce the kind of droppings seen in this photograph will develop well. It is a comical sight to see with how much agility they try to keep their nest clean.

Watery droppings

With the transition from crop milk to solid food the droppings may become very watery. This is related to excessive drinking by the parents. The cause may be a shortage of electrolytes, which are moisture-conducting substances.

Ring book

In the Netherlands all the rings issued are entered in the annual ring list. This guide, which is compiled under the supervision of the national organization, also contains other much topical information. Such a guide does not exist in Belgium. In that country the ring numbers begin with the figure for the province. For example, the first figure of all the rings issued each year in the province of Antwerp is 6.

Loss

If the ring has to be removed for any reason, the fancier should inform the national league. The pigeon concerned must then have its wing stamped every year.

Plastic clip-on rings serve, for example, to distinguish the young from different cycles. They are also useful as a means of identification when buying or acquiring birds, certainly if we have to look after a lot of young birds and are not yet familiar with all the newcomers.

Nursing

Like all birds racing pigeons grow up quickly, but only racing pigeons possess a unique 'instrument' to assist this process: the crop or pigeon milk. The parents begin to feed the young very soon after they are hatched. They pump the squeaker full with a yellowish pulp, but they do this very carefully. The chick raises its head and instinctively seeks its way to the parent's beak. By means of an antiperistaltic movement the parents transfer the highly nutritious pap from the crop to the chick. Occasionally some is spilt. When some inexperienced fanciers see the dried-up particles at the corners of the squeaker's beak they imagine it has *trichomonosis* (canker), but this is not at all the case.

During the first days of the young bird's life the parents are mainly busy with regurgitating food. This transfer of pulp from the crop is performed by both the cock and the hen. At first it consists only of soft pap, but gradually contains more and more solid constituents.

The unique crop milk

The process of milk formation with pigeons can only be called unique. We are all familiar with the transfer of food via the beak among the various bird species, but this is always the partially digested food which the birds themselves have first picked up. Only with pigeons, and this applies to the cocks as well as the hens, does the food consist of milk which they have manufactured themselves. There are incidentally wide differences between pigeons and between pairs as far as the quantity of food is concerned and the number of days over which they maintain its production.

Milk production is controlled by the hormone prolactine which is active from the time the egg laying begins. As a result of increasingly large quantities of hormones, production reaches its peak during the first few days of milk secretion. The effect of the prolactine can be seen from about the sixth day of incubation in the thickening and furrowing of the crop. Together with a great increase in the blood supply, an accumulation of fat occurs in the cells of the crop. The crop is at its fattest from about the fifteenth day of incubation until about a week after hatching.

What is really occurring is a tremendous increase in tissue. The crop of an adult pigeon at rest weighs about 1.7 grammes. After 24 hours of milk secretion the weight is 15 grammes. But there is also a tremendous quantity of milk supplied to the young: 50 to 70 per cent of the bird's bodyweight or, to put it another way, on the fourth day, double the weight of the crop!

Milk secretion begins towards the end of the incubation period when cells on the inside of the crop become active. In these cells, as we have seen, an accumulation of fat occurs. The pigeon milk consists in part of 8.6% fat, 12.4% animal protein and 1.4% minerals. It does not contain any sugars.

From the fourth day predigested grain is added to the milk or pap. As every fancier knows, the proportion of solids gradually increases, but there are great differences between individual birds in this respect. Moreover, too little research has been carried out to be able to indicate the exact duration of the production of the lumpy, whitish yellow, cheeselike milk and the moment of transition to feeding with grain. Experiments have even found traces of milk in a pigeon 35 days after the birth of a chick.

Rate of growth

A young pigeon grows very quickly. The weight at birth is about 14 grammes, after the first day 21 grammes, after two days 34 grammes, after three days 46 grammes, after four days 63 grammes. This tremendous growth rate subsequently slows down somewhat and there is even a slight reduction with the changeover from milk to grain. But between the twelfth and the seventeenth day they again grow rapidly.

As soon as the squeakers begin to leave the nest and make valiant efforts to use their wings the period of rapid growth is over. Instead there is a gradual increase in bodyweight. It is a good idea to put some additional food in a tray in the nesting box to accustom the squeakers as soon as possible to eating independently.

Let us look for a moment at the parents. There are some born feeders among them. It sometimes happens that a cock still feeds a 35-day-old hen, but the relationship between them has meanwhile become something different from that of father to daughter.

The growth of pigeons illustrated in three photographs. From top to bottom, at the age of seven days, a week later and a week later again.

On their own feet

On about the twenty-fourth or -fifth day the young pigeons have reached the age for standing on their own feet away from the care of their parents. This stage is called weaning. The young birds have passed babyhood and are beginning their youth which, in human terms, leads rapidly to maturity. Training can start then.

Weaning

The way to independence is eased if a few young birds are removed from their parents at the same time. This is better than removing a couple each day. A small age difference among them does not matter very much, which is not to say that the youngsters will not feel strange in their new loft on the first day and eat little. But this soon passes. A number will already be pecking eagerly by the next feed. Give them an ordinary mixture and make sure they eat everything that is put before them. It is also very important that the young birds should drink well. If the drinker is normally above floor level, it should now be put on the floor. And if a doleful young pigeon is sitting on one side, blinking its eyes, put its head in the drinker. It is a necessary aid to ensure that the creature will come to the table the next time.

With the hens

We can also place young pigeons of 14 to 16 days old together with the hens in the young birds compartment. The hens will then see to it that all the offspring grow up well. It is essential to supply sufficient food for the nursing hen. The young birds quickly learn to peck *and* drink independently. When the young are between 23 and 25 days old the parent hens have to be removed, as otherwise they will continue feeding, and that is not the intention.

Date of weaning

Many fanciers examine the density of plumage under the wings and determine the date of weaning from that. The wing of the young bird in the left-hand photograph is clearly not yet fully grown, so it must remain with its parents a little longer. The owner of the wing on the right is ready for weaning and can stand on its own feet.

Upbringing

Birds which come to the hand are a joy to own, but it is vital to have a relationship of trust between the pigeons and their fancier if they are to excel in racing. One is hardly surprised when one goes into pigeon lofts for the first time and sees the birds quietly and curiously following the movements of their owner. That is how it should be in pigeon racing, but the fancier has worked hard at establishing that relationship. Like other birds, pigeons are by nature shy.

If an owner makes an effort from the moment that the young birds stand on their own feet, he is soon rewarded by the young rascals' behaviour. They come and perch on him, peck at his ears, shoelaces or trousers, get in the way when he is cleaning the loft, defend themselves against his hands and willingly allow themselves to be picked up. These and other playfully learned activities are achieved with the feeding tin in the hand. Training begins when the pigeons are five weeks old and still easily conditioned, i.e. can be taught that a particular action brings a reward. Whistling and eating go together, or rattling the tin and eating. We make use of this to teach the birds to come in quickly after a race.

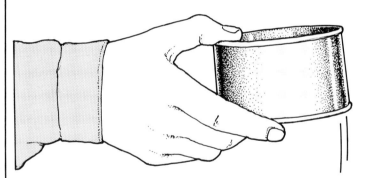

A reward encourages nearly every pigeon to play with its owner and trust him.

Whistling and the rattle of the feeding tin are suitable sounds for conditioning young pigeons from an early age.

A young pigeon must become familiar with its owner's hands. Often picking them up carefully teaches them that one does not wish them any harm.

Devotion and . . . patience

The fancier who has a reserve of patience is a fortunate man, because, as with people, there are individual differences among racing pigeons. Thus the owner who wishes to win the trust of all the young birds will need much patience as well as devotion to gain the attachment of even the most reserved youngster. The latter may soon be the one to land first on the flap after the race, in which case it is vital that no precious time be lost in hestitation because a 'stranger' wants to pick him up. Attachment and the urge to reach the safety of the loft are reflected in performance. One hundred per cent good health also plays a part, of course, and is to be observed, for example, in the urge to fly, from the white beak wattles and the white bodies.

Function of the sputnik

A sputnik and a 'quick timer' are not only excellent means of getting the birds in after the race, they also enable the young birds to familiarize themselves with the surroundings without being able to fly away immediately if something alarms them. A run in a loft for young pigeons serves the same purpose. The pigeons can be at liberty there the whole day without causing a nuisance to the neighbourhood. Lastly, it is an excellent spot for a bath.

Early pigeons/winter young

In order to be able to have available sexually mature young birds at the beginning of the young pigeons season, we must ensure that we have eggs being laid at or around Christmas. This winter breeding is particularly popular in Belgium, where the racing season for the young birds also begins two months earlier than in the Netherlands, namely, at the beginning of May.

With early pigeons or winter young the moulting process progresses well. Winter young soon renew their small plumage, but delay the dropping of their flight feathers which means that they still have a full wing for competition flights. The offspring of parents paired at the beginning of January also largely follow this moulting pattern. Winter young do require a rigorous training at a time when they are not yet paying attention to the opposite sex and, in the Netherlands, the advantages scarcely outweigh the extra trouble. It seems likely, therefore, that winter breeding will be superseded by early breeding, which means pairing on about 15 January.

Wing comparison

The wing in the left-hand photograph belongs to a young pigeon born at the end of December. It is not yet complete. At the time when the photograph was taken (June) it had not yet dropped any flight feathers. This obviously has advantages for the sport.

The other photograph shows the wing of a young bird born in March. By June three or four flight feathers have often already been dropped. At the time of the races the pigeon drops the sixth and seventh flights, which naturally handicaps it somewhat, certainly if the moult of the plumage also begins on a large scale.

Late young/summer young

Late young are generally used to strengthen the existing colony. An expert racer often needs the young from the first and second cycles for himself, so that they are usually not available for other people. Someone who applies later has more chance of obtaining offspring from the better pigeons. A favourable time for good, new blood in the ranks is also the time when the widowers are remated.

These late young must have the chance to develop properly before we pass a verdict on them. They are usually less suitable for the sport because we are unable to give them a proper preliminary training during the winter. If we do wish to fly them it is worth considering training them as yearlings with the young birds and racing them at the end of the season. If you do acquire them to strengthen the loft, keep them only for breeding.

Young birds, and pigeons are no exception, develop very quickly, much more so than other creatures.

Yearlings

A pigeon born in 1985 becomes a yearling in 1986. In the Netherlands the yearlings are entered in the same compeition as the older birds. In Belgium it is possible for yearlings to race against birds of their own age, in the conviction that there is a difference in performance. Yearlings are nevertheless capable of outstanding feats, as is shown by the results of even the great national events. But the appropriate distances for this category are under 500 kilometres.

Two-year-olds

From the above it will be clear what is meant by a two-year-old. Separate races are very occasionally held for this age category. We may demand outstanding performances from racing pigeons of this age and if they do not deliver we must fear that we have birds of inferior quality for the sport. Only with a few very slow developing long-distance strains do we tolerate waiting until the age of three years.

Breeds with the title of 'strain'

Although this book is a guide and not a portrait gallery of pigeon racing greats, we should be failing if we did not end the chapter on breeding with a few examples. Examples of pigeons where the theory of heredity has been put into practice with excellent results. Because the pigeons bear their name, we also give the names of the breeders who, aware of the theory but certainly also on the basis of sound intuition, achieved these splendid results. We are, in fact, still dealing with breeds, although in the examples given it is customary always to give them the title 'race'. We follow this custom, if only because these breeds have expanded over the years to form solid entities which deserve the name of race.

Examples

In our sport we frequently refer to race X or race Y. In most instances we are referring to the breed of a particular loft, a breed in which the owner/breeder has established a number of crossing and inbreeding characteristics which are proportionately well represented in his pigeons.

The most famous race is undoubtedly that of the Janssen Brothers from Arendonk. Even those with only a passing acquaintance with the sport know the name and refer admiringly to it. Other races worthy of that title are: Tournier, Aarden, DeSmet Matthijs, J. van Limpt, Bricoux, Van Wanroy, Delbar, van der Wegen, Catrijsse, Berlenger, Wegge and Stichelbaut. These are names of today, but also from the distant past. But you can also participate in breed formation on a small scale, in your own loft, and breed pigeons with outstanding characteristics, alert specimens able to hold their own in races and give the owner a lot of pleasure.

The Janssen family

may be regarded as the most widely disseminated strain in the world. And not without reason. Countless fanciers owe their success directly or indirectly to the work of the men in Belgium's Arendonk. These pigeons are also first-class material for crossing with any other breed or family.

The Jan Aarden family
is mainly known for the spectacular achievements of birds in long-distance flights. Many outstanding birds have been bred from Jan Aarden's 'stayers'.

Catrijsse
The Catrijsse brothers created a world-famous breed of heavy long-distance fliers. When conditions are particularly bad these birds are in their element.

Tournier pigeons
are known as birds who will have a go at everything, whatever the weather. One of the many people who have had great success with this race was Arie van den Hoek, who also became famous through his writings.

The DeSmet Matthijs family
is linked indissolubly with such names as *Kapoen*, *Genaaide* and *Oude Rijk*. Roger has not unsuccessfully continued the breeding activities of his father Valère.

Fabry pigeons

The Liège pharmacists, Fabry, father and son, have had their own strain of pigeons since before the war. The strain is particularly popular in West Germany. Fabrys are known for their beauty and all-round qualities.

The Van Wanroy race

has also made a name for itself in long-distance races. The most famous bird of the loft is the '90', but such birds as *de Spin* and *de Westerhuis* have also made the loft at Broekhuizenvorst a legend in the Dutch long-distance world.

Delbar

The family from Ronse (Renaix) was very successful in the Belgian national long-distance races shortly before and after the war. Old Delbars are usually blue and blue/white flights and chequered. Many Dutch exhibition pigeons have Delbar blood.

Horemans

The gamekeeper from Schoten, Corneel Horemans, was well-known for his fantastic, usually dark-coloured pure-bred birds. These pigeons showed a tremendous vitality.

Records

Breeding is not possible without keeping some form of records. The form they take does not matter, whether in handsome, commercially-produced diaries, in an ordinary exercise or scrapbook, or by means of the home computer. Do not trust too much to your own memory, even though it may still be in good condition. Another administrative 'document' is a pocket diary to record the preparations for important races.

Data

The minimum requirement is to keep notes of the parents with their young. It is also a good idea to keep a record of the circumstances under which the birds have performed well: position of the nest, incubation, eight-day-old youngsters, jealousy, showing good form etc. The prize itself, the number of pigeons in a race and the weather conditions may also be relevant when it comes to selection.

All kinds of 'books' can be bought for keeping pigeon records. Make a habit from the beginning of making punctual entries in a diary of this kind or, if necessary, in an exercise book.

Records

Some fanciers possess a capacious memory. One has only to give them a key word and it is like opening up a whole index of references. But they will also nearly always have some form or other of written record. Fanciers who own a computer can best join forces with a colleague who enjoys operating the keyboard to obtain the 'pigeon software'. In this way they can make use of its capacious memory for racing and breeding data.

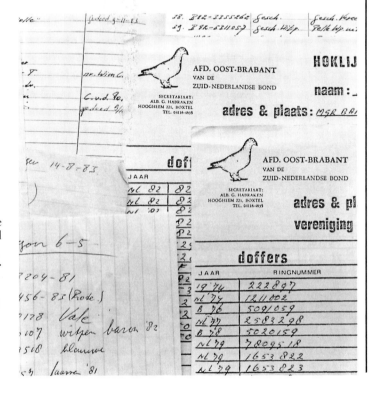

Veterinary care

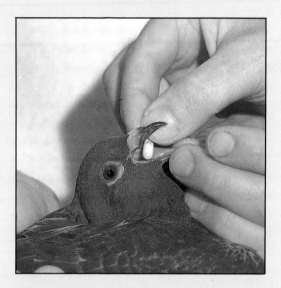

For really sick racing pigeons there is always the vet. But the fancier can do his bit: his alertness and attention can prevent a lot of heartache and reduce the number of visits to the vet.

The roles of vet and fancier

This chapter gives a review of the most important causes of sickness and the damage they can do. A few general remarks are added about treatment. Detailed veterinary information has no place in a handbook and there is no place in the hobby for do-it-yourself doctoring, unless one is a qualified vet. We should not take it upon ourselves to experiment with really sick pigeons, but should take them to the vet, preferably to one who specializes in pigeons. This chapter does not, therefore, contain any cures nor does it list the contents of a medicine cupboard. It is much more important to indicate here how the fancier can judge the health of his pigeons. The means by which he can promote the health of his birds and give first aid also merit a place in a practical guide.

The vet will first form an opinion about the pigeon's general condition. If he is familiar with pigeons he will also know how to hold them in the correct manner.

The false trail of diagnosis

Diagnosis – the evaluation of symptoms of illness – is the task of experts, just as the prescription of medicines is a matter for specialists. Symptoms can put the layman on a false trail. Diarrhoea, for example, may be caused by bacteria or viruses, but nerves, as when the cock and hen are separated, or bad digestion, could also be the cause.

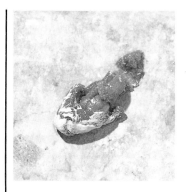

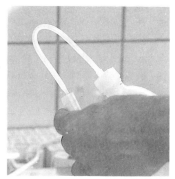

On their long path through the pigeon's body the droppings gather a wealth of data. The expert has the help of instruments to examine the droppings.

For the purposes of the examination the vet mixes the droppings brought to him by the fancier with a salt solution.

He places the tube with the salt solution and droppings in a centrifuge. The rotation causes any disease germs to collect at the top of the tube from where they can be removed for study by the vet under the microscope.

Information from the droppings

A vet makes good use of the information he derives from the droppings, but they are also a good indicator for the fancier of his colony's state of health. This applies particularly to the night droppings. They must be dry and fine and leave no traces behind after they have been picked up. The colour of the droppings is less important. It is related to what the pigeons have eaten and what they are doing. A pigeon on its way home makes green droppings because of the effect of the digestive juices secreted by the liver. The droppings produced during the day are less significant. Nerves, for example, among pigeons going into the basket for the first time, can cause whole pools of liquid. A visit to a gutter or a pond also produces watery droppings, but always during the day not at night.

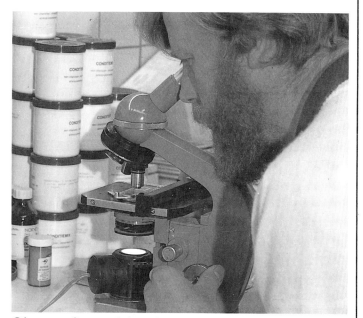

Signs of good health

Healthy pigeons drop their first flight feather as a rule when they are nursing and brooding at the same time. When pairing around the beginning of the year, this happens on about 1 March. With later pairing and therefore later nursing and brooding, this date is obviously correspondingly later. Other signs of good health are the steady progress of the moult, regular and punctual egg laying and the fact that the hens become more attractive after they have laid. An eye should be kept on squeakers which are behind in their development, remain bald for a long time, have a coarse plumage and squeak and squirt their droppings.

Prevention

The fancier cannot have healthy pigeons without putting in a bit of effort. The basic conditions for a healthy colony are first-class housing (Chapter 2) and a varied diet (Chapter 3). Another safeguard is to avoid races which go beyond the strength of the individual pigeon because the birds inevitably run more risks during the flight than in their own carefully managed loft. Far away from home they may come into contact with dirty ground litter or a neighbour's sick pigeons. In addition, the fancier must invest extra time in maintaining the hygiene of the loft.

A final point: paying attention to the health of the birds is no cause for fear and panic. The running beak or wet eye of the young pigeon are no more serious than the fancier's own cold. Neither are necessarily harbingers of serious ills. If we have provided a good environment, much can be left to nature itself. Immediately dosing with medicines, prescribed or otherwise, does the birds no good in the long run. 'Blind courses of treatment', the administering of preventive medicine on the fancier's own responsibility, does no harm provided it does not happen too often. But it is better to intervene only when the need has been demonstrated. Then the picture of the real state of the pigeons' health remains unclouded and their performance will not be slowly, but surely, undermined.

A well-constructed and maintained loft will spare our pigeons a lot of misery.

The living quarters

Right at the construction stage we can take various measures in the interests of the pigeons' health. The air circulation can be planned in such a way, for example, that the stale air is immediately removed. Air circulation, incidentally, is not the same thing as draught! Pigeons consume 600 litres of air per day in order to manufacture 300 litres of pure oxygen.

We can also ensure that the sun's rays, which have such a stimulating effect on young and old pigeons, can easily penetrate into the loft. Congestion must be avoided at any cost. Each pair of pigeons requires about three-quarters of a cubic metre of space.

Provision for a regular bath ensures that the feathers are cleaned, and the addition of a bath salt gives external parasites less opportunity to establish themselves. The water must be thrown away and the floor dried immediately after the bath. Lastly, in building or rebuilding the loft particular attention must be paid to keeping it dry, so that disease germs have less chance to breed, and to reducing excessive temperature fluctuations.

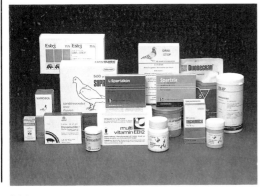

Medicines belong to the vet's store cupboard. They can be a great help in the treatment of disorders provided the directions are followed.

Eating and drinking

Infected droppings, mucus secretion and dust can pollute the drinking water. It is a good idea, therefore, to change the drinking water and clean the drinking vessels daily. For feeding, a covered feeding trough is recommended. By giving food on the floor, even if it has been thoroughly cleaned beforehand, we are running unnecessary risks. The pigeons may foul the food with droppings while they are eating. Also, there may be all kinds of pests lurking in the joints and crevices which are not so easily swept away.

Disinfection

Once the loft has been erected with proper provision for the health of the birds, it must be properly maintained in the interests of disease prevention. This is achieved by regularly disinfecting the quarters once or twice a year, after the great clean-out. But there are fanciers who disinfect the loft much more often. Disinfectants are available in the trade. It is recommended that the directions for use be read carefully first.

There are also the old, well-tried remedies, such as lime milk, which is made up by adding kitchen salt and a half litre of creoline to twenty litres of water. A solution of two to five per cent soda – protect your hands, eyes and clothes – applied hot, is very effective against virus diseases. The cocci worm cannot tolerate ammonia, so that this is also a good remedy, to be used in a five per cent solution. Lysol and creoline should also be used in the same proportion.

Infection by domestic animals

The combination of racing pigeons and domestic pets is not always a good idea as far as the health of the pigeons is concerned, which is not to say that combining them will necessarily result in the transfer of germs. Some fanciers have not experienced any problems from the proximity of other animals, but other swear 'never again' after some bad experience.

Rabbits in general cause no problems, provided they are not housed in the pigeons' quarters. This causes smell and damp, although there are remedies against them. Some fanciers have regretted keeping rabbits in their lofts.

Chickens have a bad effect on pigeons who frequent the same places. Worms and red mite, as well as pigeon pox, diphtheria and coccidiosis may be the result. On the other hand, there are also places where combining the two causes no problems.

Other animals Dogs generally stay in the house and so are no problem. Cats and pigeons are natural enemies, although there are splendid examples of peaceful co-existence, but the felines must have come into the household at a very early age. Cats may also do useful work as hunters of those other threats to the pigeons' health: rats and mice. It is better not to keep canaries and other birds with the pigeons.

Resistance

Disease may be regarded as the defeat of the pigeon's body by the cause of the ailment. The greater the resistance, the longer the organism will maintain itself. Pigeons possess this resistance, this *immunity*, to some extent by nature, but the degree to which they do so varies greatly from bird to bird, even within the same loft.

Older pigeons are, in general, less susceptible than young birds. Resistance is increased if the bird, whether or not assisted by medication, has withstood an attack by disease germs, with the struggle by the white blood corpuscles resulting in the development of antibodies. The latter can give a lifelong resistance against some viruses, but the protection against parasites is usually only of short duration and often ineffective. This partial immunity is sometimes called *premunition* and it is a pity that it is precisely the parasites which are responsible for many attacks on the racing pigeon's health.

Conditions for immunization

Modern vaccines guarantee a good resistance against the disease for which the vaccination is being given, but only healthy pigeons should be vaccinated since vaccination introduces a disease, even if only a very mild one, and sick birds cannot take another disease 'on top'.

Pigeons may be feverish for a few days after the injection, so it is best to allow them some rest. Loft occupants who have resisted the attack of a particular disease have built up a natural resistance to it, so that they do not need to be immunized. Vaccinations are in general given to young birds, which means that in time all the pigeons will have a turn. But it may happen that a hitherto more or less unknown disease strikes, as happened in the recent past with the paramixo virus. At such a time it may be decided to immunize the total population of the lofts. In such cases the vaccination is often carried out on an organized basis. Pigeons may require a regular booster injection at intervals to maintain immunity.

Suspect pigeons

Sick pigeons and those about whose health we are uncertain should not be allowed to mix with their companions and should be kept separate. In order not to expose other fanciers' birds to unnecessary risks, only healthy pigeons may be put into the baskets for races or shows. Cleaning the compartments where the suspect birds are demands extra time and care, since they are the breeding grounds of germs and vermin. We also keep stray pigeons separate in order to avoid all risks.

It is advisable to plan our lofts to allow for pigeons to be segregated. This applies, for example, to birds whose health is a cause for concern. It is also better to segregate other fanciers' pigeons which have come to take refuge with us. A separate compartment is also necessary when a bird has a fracture which is healing.

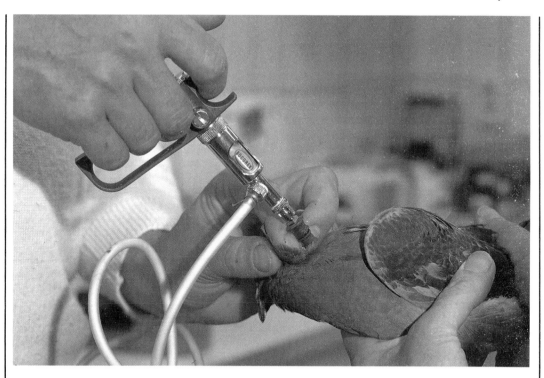

Vaccination

With vaccination resistance is developed forcibly, as it were. The vaccine, obtained from weakened or dead bacteria or viruses, stimulates the organism to create antibodies. This gives the pigeon an active immunity which protects it against the disease for which it has been vaccinated. There are three important vaccinations: against paratyphoid (in December/ January for old pigeons and six weeks before the races for the young birds); against pigeon pox and diphtheria (for young birds at the age of five to six weeks and during the following winter); and against the paramixo virus. The latter vaccination is spread over the winter, preferably at a minimum age of six weeks for young birds and at about four to six weeks before the first race.

While the fancier lends a helping hand the vet injects drugs directly into the blood stream.

With large-scale inoculations or those organized on a club basis an injection gun is useful.

Vitamins

These 'vital substances', which were discussed in detail in the chapter on feeding, are indispensable not only for Man but for the pigeon. Extra vitamins are necessary after the birds have been given antibiotics. The vitamins concerned include vitamin A, D_3 and the B group. Fanciers who add preventive medicines to the drinking water should also bear in mind that these demand extra vitamins of the pigeon's organism.

Classification by type

The wide range of causes of disease may be divided into a number of groups. If we look at the cases with which fanciers may have to deal, the most important are: the viruses, the bacteria and the parasites. The latter are divided into internal and external parasites or vermin. From the scientific point of view there are more groups, such as the moulds, but of the latter only *aspergillosis*, an infection of the lungs and air sacs, sometimes affects pigeons. There are also intermediate forms, such as *infectious coryza* (between viruses and bacteria) and other scientific refinements. The classification below, however, is based on the everyday experience of the pigeon fancier.

Clinically healthy

means that the pigeons have been cured of the disease from which they were suffering, but that they are still a source of infection in one way or another. This occurs, for example, with *intestinal salmonellosis*. The droppings contain germs of the microbe which is the cause of the disease. If these get into the food and drinking water, this may cause the other pigeons – and their owner – incalculable misery.

	treatment/prevention
viruses	
paramixo	vaccine
pigeon pox	vaccine
diphtheria	vaccine/eye ointment
one-eye cold	rest/drops/eye ointment
intermediate group	
infectious coryza	appropriate drugs
bacteria	
paratyphoid	appropriate drugs
internal parasites	
trichomoniasis	appropriate drugs
coccidiosis	appropriate drugs
worms	appropriate drugs
external parasites	
ticks, mites and lice	agents for external use/ disinfectants/baths

This summary is not a scientific breakdown of all the ills and diseases which can afflict the loft. The intention is to set out only the most common. Under the heading 'combatting', loft hygiene may be regarded as a preventive measure in almost all cases. When antibiotics are administered additional vitamins should also be given.

Paramixo virus

This virus sickness first struck Belgium and the Netherlands in the winter of 1982/83 and immediately became the pigeon fancier's number one enemy. The attack was unexpected, merciless and on a massive scale. It claimed many young and old pigeons as its victims and there was some panic. Scientists worked feverishly at developing and distributing a vaccine. In early 1983 the NPO (Dutch Racing Pigeon Owners Association) decided on compulsory inoculation (inoculation is not compulsory in Belgium). The vaccine which was developed works very effectively. Pigeons which are not inoculated, however, are doomed to die. The disease is caused by a 'relative' of a virus which has long been known among poultry, Newcastle disease.

External symptoms

With infected birds the symptoms mainly affect the brain, showing themselves in loss of balance and associated inability to fly, the head falling to one side and pecking alongside the food. Also the droppings are watery.

Treatment

The only treatment is preventative, by means of vaccination (old birds in the winter and young birds in April/May). (See also general notes on vaccination.)

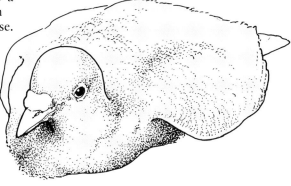

The consequence of infection by the dreaded paramixo virus is a deterioration in the functioning of the nervous system, which may cause disturbance of balance.

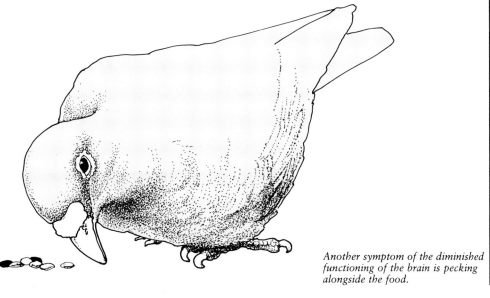

Another symptom of the diminished functioning of the brain is pecking alongside the food.

Pigeon pox

Until a few years ago, when it 'suddenly' attacked during the spring months, this was a true summer disease. It usually has a mild character and occurs mainly among young pigeons. That it occurs mainly in the summer is a logical consequence of the fact that its principal carrier is the gnat, which is active at that time of year. The insect drinks the blood of an infected pigeon and carries the virus to the next cock or hen it bites. Lofts situated close to the sea are less troubled by the disease because gnats are less common there. The relationship of pigeon pox to gnats is also shown by the fact that true pox years had summers in which these insects were observed in large numbers.

A less common cause of infection is the blood-sucking pigeon tick. The virus may also find a home in injuries to the skin or the mucous membrane of the bill, caused during a fight. It is always the pigeon pox virus from a fellow pigeon which causes the disease, as pigeons are immune to viruses from other animals.

External symptoms

Pigeons which are suffering from pigeon pox appear unsightly because of skin swellings, particularly on the head, but after about three weeks, when the swellings have dried up or slowly fallen off, the misery is past. Usually at least, because there *may* be permanent damage to the horny bill. Pigeon pox around the eyes may cause discoloration, but this does not affect the bird's racing performance once the illness is over.

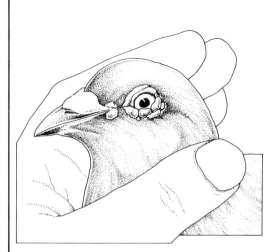

Skin swellings give the pigeon an unattractive appearance, although this passes after about three weeks.

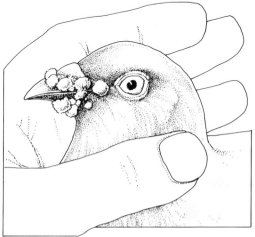

The outward signs of pigeon pox may also appear on the beak. Leave the pustules well alone as it only leads to further infection.

In order to be able to give an injection some feathers are removed from the thigh bone, thereby exposing the follicles.

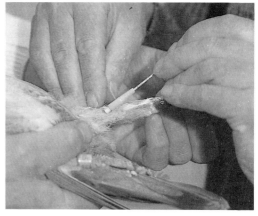

The vet then paints the vaccine over the exposed part with a stiff brush.

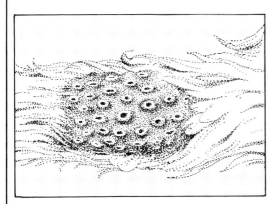

Enlarged follicles
No changes can be observed on the first day after the vaccine has been painted on. Around the fifth day the enlarged follicles show that the vaccine is active. Feverish swellings appear. By about the tenth day everything is normal again.

Treatment

of pigeon pox around the eyes with eye ointment is to be recommended, and prevents worse things. Otherwise it is best to let nature take its course. If you have your young birds inoculated twice every year (four to six weeks before the races and the following winter – see above) your loft will be under control as far as pigeon pox is concerned.

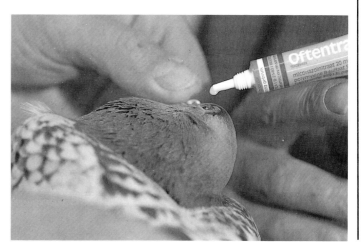

Diphtheria

Diphtheria is caused by the same virus as pigeon pox. It is mainly the adult birds which fall victim to this internal form of the virus. The infected birds get yellow film in the beak and throat which can cause breathing difficulties. In the worst cases this leads to asphyxiation. Once the symptoms of diphtheria have appeared there is little to do but wait. Pigeon pox vaccine is also effective against diphtheria.

Infectious coryza

This disease may appear in very different forms: simple infections with scarcely any symptoms or cases with breathing difficulties. It is a question of whether complications occur, such as severe infection by a parasite-borne disease (coccidiosis, trichomoniasis) or by other disease germs. Exhausted and diseased birds often form fresh sources of infection.

If the pigeon looks like this it is generally unhesitatingly regarded as a symptom of infectious coryza, although aggravating factors often play a role.

External characteristics

With inflammation of the mucous membrane there will at first be only 'dry snot', without secretion in the nose and eyes. (Sometimes moisture or pus are formed in the beak, nose and eyes and the beak wattles become wet.) The throat becomes red and sometimes the trachea, air sacs and lungs are infected. The pigeons scratch their beak and head. They sneeze and have runny noses, which may develop into rattling and coughing.

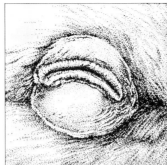

Left: illustration of an infected eye with inflammation of the cornea and prolapse of the third eyelid. Right: swollen, red eyelids.

Treatment

must be carried out by the vet. He will usually prescribe antibiotics to be added to the drinking water or give an injection. The fancier should meanwhile check whether the general hygiene in the loft is adequate, or whether there is congestion and/or the birds are not being entered for races which overtax their strength. He must particularly check whether the loft is draughty. If it is there will soon be a repetition of the outbreak if nothing is done.

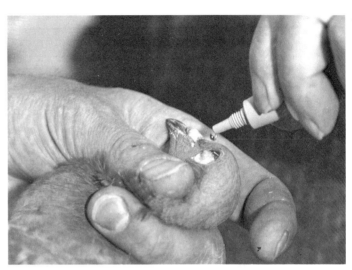

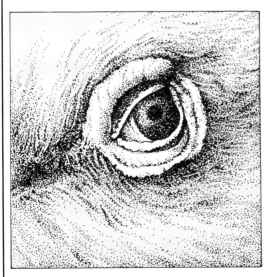

One-eye cold

This popular name is derived from the most conspicuous symptom of the disease, which affects young pigeons, namely, the watery eye. Bacteria bring complications in the form of seriously inflamed eyelids, which may even stick together. It is striking how much the susceptibility to one-eye cold varies from loft to loft.

With the simple form nature will run its course, but with other forms a period of rest of at least two weeks is needed for the whole loft. Apart from the danger of infecting other fanciers' birds, including pigeons with the disease in the travelling basket may lead to serious losses.

Salmonellosis/ Paratyphoid

This disease has a variety of symptoms, all of which are equally serious. (Incidentally, not only pigeons but also Man can be infected, even if only rarely, by the *salmonella* microbe.) The disease derives its scientific name of *salmonellosis* from this microbe. It is better known as *paratyphoid*. The microbe sometimes multiplies so rapidly that the infected birds suffer blood poisoning which very soon leads to death. Generally speaking, however, salmonellosis is more stealthy in its nature.

With paratyphoid the vet will examine the droppings as well as the blood. Where droppings are healthy, as above, this is unnecessary. Diseased droppings, not only of pigeons suffering from paratyphoid, are watery.

In recent years there has been an increasing number of cases of this disease in its various forms. In particular many more cases of intestinal salmonellosis are being identified than previously. The form in question is a pure one, i.e. the disease is restricted to the intestiness. It is striking that paratyphoid strikes most often in the autumn, during the moult.

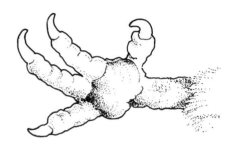

Paratyphoid may also establish itself in the pigeon's legs, particularly in the joints. It causes swellings which eventually deprive the bird of its freedom of movement.

External symptoms

Seats of the disease are the intestines, joints, sexual organs and, to a lesser extent, the brain and middle ear. In the latter case there will be twisted neck and signs of paralysis in the rest of the body. With inflammation of the intestines the pigeons will become feverish and thirsty and be affected by green diarrhoea. As they lose their appetite they will become thinner and thinner. Many pigeons succumb. Those who survive are often clinically healthy and so represent a danger to their companions in the loft.

Infertility is the result of infection of the male sexual organs. Infertility among the hens depends on the number of microbes which have

established themselves in the ovary. If eggs are laid, the young will be ailing or carriers of the disease.

A hanging wing may also be a symptom of this disease. (It may also be paralysis of the wing, but the vet will consider this in his diagnosis.) Paratyphoid in the leg joints causes the bird to limp because it will be suffering from inflammation and swelling. Later there will be stiffening and loss of freedom of movement.

Hanging wing

One of the many external symptoms of paratyphoid is hanging wing, caused by infection of the wing joints. This must not be confused with *basaliom* or blood wart, a swelling of a benign character.

Twisted neck
A pocket of paratyphoid in the head may result in the condition known as 'twisted neck'. This is not the best known symptom of the disease.

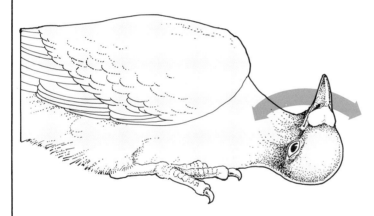

Treatment

is a matter for the vet. For intestinal salmonellosis he will prescribe antibiotics and sulphonamides. He is also qualified to carry out a specialized investigation of blood and droppings to ascertain to what extent the loft is infected. Measures against the disease are mainly preventative ones: vaccination and, in view of the cyclic nature of the infection, hygiene and more hygiene. Droppings or blood tests may also be carried out.

A blood test for paratyphoid begins with a prick in the leg.

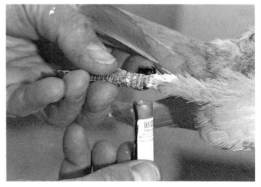

The vet allows the blood to drip into a tube to be taken away for examination.

Coccidiosis

This is a form of intestinal inflammation caused by the *cocci worm*, a single-celled parasite. The *oocysts*, the first stage in the worm's growth, are found in the droppings of infected birds. They come from the pigeon's intestines and are harmless until they come into contact with the outside air. They then ripen, in two or three days at summer temperatures, longer during colder weather. If the oocysts are again taken up by a pigeon they begin to parasitize on the intestines. Intestinal cells are destroyed and a new infection cycle begins.

Very wet droppings are also a sign to the fancier to be on the alert.

External symptoms

Young pigeons suffer greatly from this disease. Severe diarrhoea causes them to lose a lot of weight and they sometimes die. The course of the disease is less serious for weaned birds, but they still suffer from weakening of their physical condition as a whole. Symptoms of this are that moulting stops, their legs weaken and the breastbones are bent. Adult pigeons are generally little affected by coccidiosis, although they may succumb to it when they are in an exhausted condition after a race. At such times they lose weight, their plumage becomes dull, their beak wattles turn grey and their throat becomes mucous.

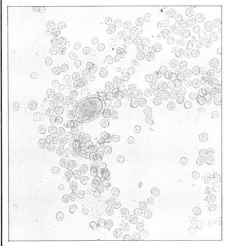

Administering a capsule

Drugs in capsule form must be pushed well to the back of the throat. Swallowing can be encouraged by stroking downwards across the throat.

Treatment

is possible thanks to good drugs which leave the wall of the intestine intact. But they must be given in good time. As always, prevention is much better than having to cure the disease. Oocysts are light and easily float upwards, so that drinkers should be placed well above the floor. It is also important to clean feeding troughs, drinkers etc. when cleaning the loft. Dry conditions are also important, since the oocysts ripen only when there is sufficient humidity and oxygen.

Microscope picture of oocysts, the first stage in the life of cocci worms.

Eggs of the thread worm, one of the round worms (right); below, the internal parasite itself. Not so long ago this worm was particularly feared because there were no effective remedies against it.

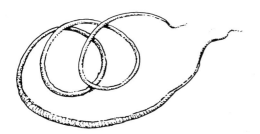

Small tape worm
The eggs of this flat worm require a second host before they can develop into larvae and pass on the infection.

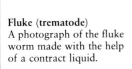

Fluke (trematode)
A photograph of the fluke worm made with the help of a contract liquid.

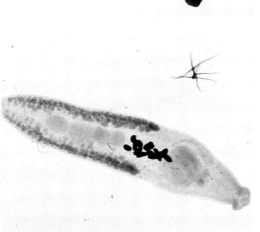

Thread worms

Of all the parasitic worms we should be most on guard against the thread worm, which attacks the health of the pigeons in large numbers. It does this in the wall of the small intestine. The presence of thread worms there causes inflammation, which leads in the mildest cases to a loss of condition and in the worst cases to death. In contrast to many other diseases and disorders, the threadworm is not spread only by members of the same species.

There are now effective remedies against the thread worm, even for seriously affected cases. As so often, however, good hygiene can prevent a lot of misery.

Other worms

Large round worms, known as roundworms, establish themselves in the small intestine. They abstract foodstuffs from their 'host' and secrete poisonous substances which find their way into the bloodstream and reduce the bird's digestive ability, usually resulting in diarrhoea and anaemia. Tape worms do not give much trouble. Flukes are almost unknown in Belgium, but rather more common in the Netherlands. This is because of the presence of large areas of water and the associated population of snails, which are the fluke's intermediate host. Older pigeons may be seriously infected and die. Squeakers may be affected by more or less serious bloody diarrhoea. Suitable remedies are available, however, against these and other worms.

Roundworm, egg stage
When the eggs have developed into round worms they become visible to the naked eye.

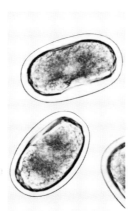

Trichomoniasis (Canker)

This parasitic disease used to be greatly feared because there was no effective remedy against it. The parasite *trichomonas gallinae* has by no means disappeared from lofts but it is now possible to combat it. Here, too, it is the young pigeons which suffer most from the sickness.

The first symptom is a heavy, sour-smelling diarrhoea. Soon afterwards yellow spots or cheeselike scabs form at the back of the throat and in the gullet. When the scabs have become so large that the bird can no longer swallow or the windpipe is compressed, death follows. This also occurs if the brain is affected from the back of the nasal cavity or if the liver is reached.

Trichomoniasis may be restricted to the back of the throat, however, in which case the squeakers lose only the hanging part of the palate, i.e. the 'teeth'. The same forms of the disease may be observed with older birds, but these usually withstand the attack. The fancier should also be on the lookout for milder forms of the disease which may all too readily get worse.

Trichomonas gallinae

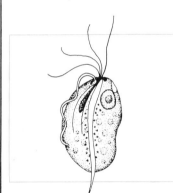

In the drawing on the left, the cause of trichomoniasis is enlarged 3,400 times. There are a number of species of this parasite and the effect they have when they establish themselves in the pigeon varies considerably, from mild to fatal. This is not to say that a slight infection should be left to run its course. Without some action from us – and excellent medicines are now available – there is a chance that the disease will return in a more serious form.

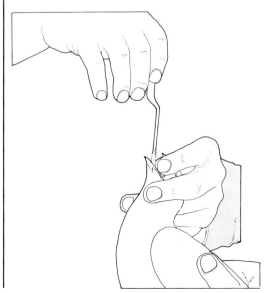

A smear
is made with the aid of a pickup with a piece of cotton wool which the vet pulls through the throat and the crop.

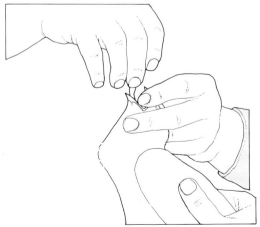

Treatment

Good remedies against trichomoniasis are available. Infection often occurs through the drinking water, so it is recommended that two drinkers be provided for each loft, to be used alternately.

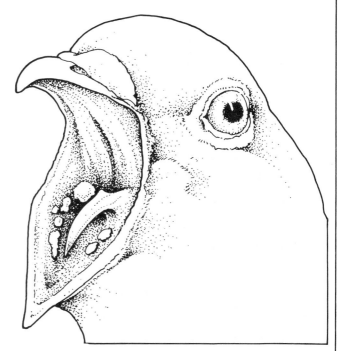

Second cycle crisis

is how we describe the infection danger resulting from bringing together the young from the first and second cycles. A seven-day course of antibiotics may be the solution for fanciers who have no other choice because of lack of space.

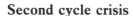

Dabbing
The vet can sometimes treat a serious throat infection by dabbing it with iodine, using a cotton wool stick. Drugs are normally given in tablet form or in the form of powder to be added to the drinking water.

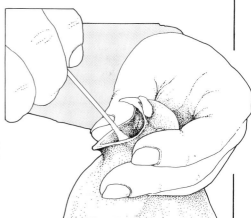

Throat sac

With trichomoniasis yellow scabs occur at the back of the throat and in the gullet. Severe swelling of the throat sac can result in suffocation.

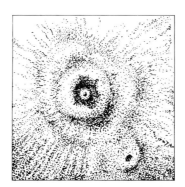

Navel

If germs are present in the nest (e.g. in spilt crop milk) they can penetrate the umbilical cord by way of the as yet unclosed navel. A cheesy scab then forms under the skin.

External parasites

External parasites occur in all shapes and sizes. The consequences of their presence in the pigeon loft needn't disturb us unduly, although we should keep a lookout for them, since their presence can lead to a deterioration in the condition of the birds, which is a good reason to combat them. The fancier can make use of effective pesticides to assist him in this.

Feathers which have been eaten away at the edge are a sign of the presence of external parasites in the loft, notably the plumage mite.

The red mite

has more or less the same behaviour as the large pigeon mite and the consequences of its blood-sucking activities are the same. Treatment is carried out in two stages: one for the adult parasites and larvae, and one for the remaining eggs which have meanwhile developed.

The large pigeon tick

sucks blood during the night and then returns to its hiding place: in cracks and joints. These are the adult ticks. The larvae attach themselves for a few days by suction to the neck and under the wings of the bird. An alert fancier will spot little dark red balls the size of a pinhead. Both ticks and their larvae cause anaemia and unrest among the birds.

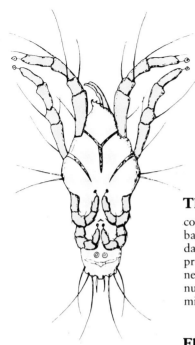

The plumage mite

consumes the barbs and barbicules of the feathers. The damage is not disastrous provided the birds are not neglected. There are incidentally numerous kinds of plumage mite.

Fleas

are rarely found on pigeons.

The feather-rot mite

has also had to give a lot of ground in recent years, which is fortunate because the mite was, and still would be if given the chance, responsible for feathers breaking off. The problem in treatment with a medication is reaching the parasites' hiding places. With large colonies, dipping the pigeon is sometimes the only solution.

The long pigeon louse
or long plumage louse, causes little damage provided there are not too many of them.

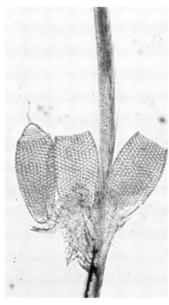

Eggs
of the long pigeon louse, clinging to the feather shaft.

Lice

are a pest that many fanciers don't worry unduly about, although they may be a little ashamed if a colleague discovers them. We must nevertheless be on guard against the disturbance which the large body louse, in particular, causes through its great mobility.

Threatening dangers

Obstacles on the way home in the form of telephone and aerial wires and flying attackers, such as sparrowhawks and kestrels, also constitute a threat to the racing pigeon's wellbeing. Shotguns can also cause damage. The fancier cannot arm his birds against these dangers and so he will find himself having to deal sooner or later with fractures and injuries resulting from undesired 'collisions'. The simplest injuries, such as superficial grazes, are best left to nature, since the skin of healthy pigeons heals readily. More serious injuries need careful treatment before being left to the natural healing process. With fractures, too, it is best not to try to deal with them ourselves.

Illustrations of a simple operation: removal of a growth on a pigeon's abdomen. After the growth has been removed, the vet closes the wound with the aid of stitches.

Wounds

Torn pectoral muscles have to be stitched. Little can be done about haemorrhages, recognisable from blue muscles under the skin. If a period of rest does not result in restoration of the tissue, parts of the pectoral muscle will atrophy and this means the end of that bird's racing career.

Healing of a torn air sac – identifiable from swellings caused by air accumulations under the skin – may sometimes be achieved by shutting the patient up for a period of ten days. Serious tears are stitched by passing a woollen thread through the skin at the site of the air sac. The thread is left in place for a few days. Pricking false air blisters gives temporary relief, but they soon fill again.

Tears at the top of the crop heal spontaneously, but tears lower down should be treated by a vet.

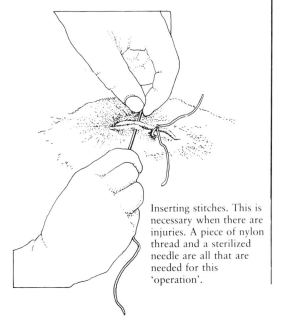

Inserting stitches. This is necessary when there are injuries. A piece of nylon thread and a sterilized needle are all that are needed for this 'operation'.

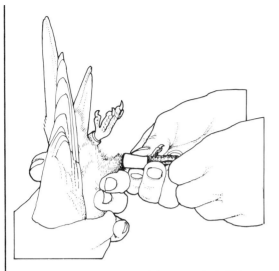

Splints may be held in place on a broken leg with the aid of a cardboard tube.

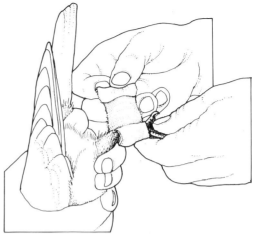

After the tube is fitted some gauze is wrapped round it.

Fractures

With leg fractures a distinction is made between open and closed fractures, i.e. between fractures where the bone protrudes through the skin and those where it does not. Open fractures are best treated by the vet. Closed fractures will heal quite quickly if the pigeon is segregated in a small compartment with little freedom of movement and given food and drink within immediate reach of its beak.

Broken legs can be put in splints and bound with clean bandages which are changed regularly.

This operation may go wrong, so it is better to restrict movement to segregating the pigeon.

It is generally better not to attempt to treat a wing fracture. Experiments with splints and bandages and the fitting of a kind of harness in which the bird must remain for about a month almost never produce a racing pigeon which is still a good flier. A serious wing fracture nearly always means the end of the racing career. The pigeon can of course be retained for breeding.

Bald breasts

are often attributed to the sharp edges of drinkers, but vets and many fanciers reject this explanation. It may be the result of a disturbance in metabolism. Anyone seeing this phenomenon should look carefully to see whether an external parasite might not be at work. Constant irritation affects the birds' condition and lowers their performance. Therapy may take the form of a three-week treatment with a mild descabbing agent. Bald breasts become apparent when pigeons inflate their crops.

Waste oil

An increasing number of pigeons and other birds fall victim to oil-polluted seawater. The body – but not the head – of the victims can be treated with a soap solution. Rinse with luke warm water and dry off with warm towels. The birds are not very presentable after their bath, but it does help. Pigeons lose a lot of fat in this way, so they must be given the opportunity to regain it.

Consequences of the modern environment: a row of pigeons, probably suffocated by a cloud of poison.

Stimulants

We are not referring here simply to extra vitamins, but to the real 'pep pills', which are also used in pigeon racing. There are two groups: amphetamines etc and the muscle-strengthening drugs (anabolic steroids). Use of these drugs demands in principle more of the organism than it has to give. This is really the main reason for rejecting them.

Apart from other considerations, there are 'technical' objections to the use of the first group, since amphetamines have a vitiating effect on the pigeon's homing ability. Moreover, they have a delayed reaction so that one needs to know in advance the point of time at which the performance has to be delivered, while, as every fancier knows, the moment of liberation can never be accurately determined. Even if one were able to administer the drugs to operate at a previously established time, such as 20 hours after putting the birds into the baskets, postponement of the release signal would mean that one had shot well wide of the mark, because performance reaches a low after the effect of the stimulant has passed its peak!

It might be possible to achieve something with one or other muscle-strengthening drug, but the success will prove to be short-lived. Moreover, racing is not just a matter of speed but of steering a direct course to the loft.

The sport

All the foregoing is really subsidiary to the sport. The person who houses, tends, manages and breeds racing pigeons makes all these efforts in order to be able to enjoy their race home. We call it the sport. And that is what it is: competition, tension, joy and disappointment. And uncertainty. Because we are racing with living creatures who still carry many secrets with them on their flights.

The races

The first and most important aim of our sport is to ensure that the pigeons return home as quickly as possible. In the preceding chapters we have emphasized how breeding, not only in a general way but sometimes very directly, is related to race performance. Think, for example, of winter breeding. And the same applies to all the other aspects of the sport. We can truthfully say that we are prepared to do a lot for our winged friends and we hope, of course, that they will not disappoint us.

Today's races have very little in common with those of our fellow sportsmen of years gone by. Then the pigeons had to be shown as soon as possible in the clubroom, where they were also on show for the remainder of the day. Few races were held and the only prize was the glory of winning. Today, as in so many other sports, money is an indispensable element. But we must add that the media lose no time in reporting exceptional prizes awarded to the winner or as a reward for a champion.

Exceptions do not make the rule. A recent investigation in Belgium, where money plays no more important part in the structure of the 'sport, shows that of the nearly 100,000 fanciers 11 per cent make a profit from races, but for threequarters of that 11 per cent the profit does not cover the costs.

To return, after this financial digression, to the history of racing. Showing the pigeons was abolished, rubber ring races were introduced and fast runners were employed to hand in the rings. Good human athletes could affect the result. (Sometimes a ring was swallowed in the haste. Then the runners had willy-nilly to put their fingers in their throats or find some other way of producing the proof of the race performance.) With the introduction of the timing clock, the device for establishing the time of the termination of the flight, romance was lost in favour of . . . more honest methods.

Now fanciers keep each other informed by telephone of the progress of the race. In the Netherlands Teletekst (Dutch Ceefax) gives the result on the television screen and the placing of thousands of pigeons throughout the country is announced with the aid of computers during the week of the race. But nothing has changed in the racing itself. It is faster, there is more specialization in long and short distances, of course, but the racing pigeon still sets course for home by the same means and we still do not know how it does it.

The pigeons are transported from the club room to the liberation point. They are waiting for the starting signal for the flight to the home lofts.

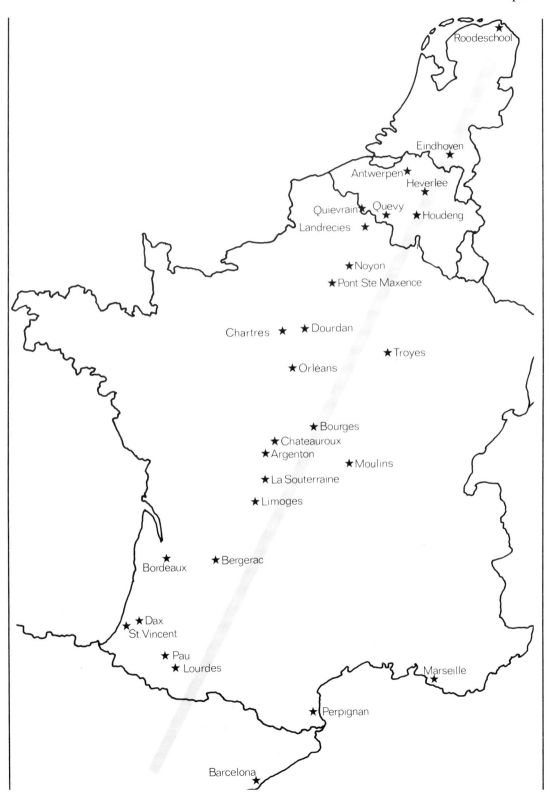

Roodeschool ★

Eindhoven ★

Antwerpen ★
Heverlee ★

Quievrain ★ ★ Quevy
★ Houdeng

Landrecies ★

★ Noyon

★ Pont Ste Maxence

Chartres ★   ★ Dourdan

★ Troyes

★ Orléans

★ Bourges
★ Chateauroux
★ Argenton   ★ Moulins
★ La Souterraine
★ Limoges

★ Bordeaux   ★ Bergerac

★ Dax
St.Vincent ★
★ Pau
★ Lourdes

★ Marseille

★ Perpignan

Barcelona ★

187

Excitement for the fancier

Every pigeon lover awaits the start of the racing season with great excitement. There is nothing finer for him than to see a pigeon return home from the race with folded wings as a reward for his efforts of the preceding winter. The anticipated speeds under particular weather conditions are engraved in his memory so that if he expects, from experience or from contact with his colleagues, that his favourite has clocked up a good time, the tension is all the greater. He knows that he has to remain calm, but the pigeon must surely feel the tension with which the race rubber is removed. The clock key turns and the waiting begins. A couple of words of thanks directed at the bird are rewarded with a gentle cooing.

But there is also the feeling of helplessness when it appears that all his efforts have been in vain. The pigeons don't fly and don't win any prizes. And yet everything was in order. What went wrong? Who can say? If one is racing well, one can give a bird a mile, so to speak, and still win. But if circumstances are against one . . . Nevertheless, love for one's pigeons, the relaxation of the loft, carry one through the difficult period. And next week there is another race. One dreams of how *then* an early pigeon will drop on the flap.

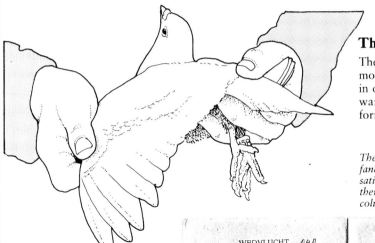

The selection

The pigeon is inspected once more for the race. Is the plumage in order, does the bird feel warm, is there any evidence of form, how is the bird's health?

The results have been recorded. The fancier can look back with satisfaction on the races, certainly if there is only one figure in the price column.

Waiting . . .

Peering into the air at that one little dot which grows ever larger and begins to fold its wings preparatory to landing . . . on our loft. But not every fancier keeps a lookout. Some are lost in thought, others pace up and down or bustle about. A few, apparently, simply continue with what they are doing or telephone all over the place. And fanciers are often grumpy and fractious, even if it is not their nature.

RACE PROGRAMME 1985
Eindhoven Competition Committee – Established 1918

Training flights

Liberation			Time and place		Distance	Basketing day	Load	No. pigeons per basket
Sat	23	Mar	07.00	Luijkgestel	24	Friday	20	35
Sat	30	Mar	07.00	Luijkgestel	24	Friday	20	35
Wed	17	Apr	07.00	Luijkgestel	24	Tuesday	20	35
Wed	5	Jun	07.00	Bergeijk	18	Tuesday	20	40
Wed	12	Jun	07.00	Luijkgestel	24	Tuesday	20	40
Tue	18	Jun	07.00	Moll	38	Monday	20	40
Wed	26	June	07.00	Aeschot	68	Tuesday	20	40
Tue	30	Jul	07.00	Moll	38	Monday	20	40
Tue	13	Aug	07.00	Bergeijk	18	Monday	20	40
Tue	20	Aug	07.00	Luijkgestel	24	Monday	20	40

Old pigeons

Liberation			Time and place		Distance	Basketing day	Load	No. pigeons per basket
Sun	7	Apr	08.00	Heverlee	84	Sat 6–4	40	35
Sun	14	Apr	08.00	Houdeng	140	Sat 13–4	40	35
Sun	21	Apr	08.00	Heverlee	84	Sat 20–4	40	35
Sun	28	Apr	08.00	Quevy	157	Sat 27–4	40	35
Sun	5	May	08.00	St Quentin	226	Sat 4–5	60	35
Sun	12	May	08.00	St Quentin	226	Sat 11–5	60	35
Thu	16	May	08.00	Houdeng	140	Wed 15–5	40	35
Sun	19	May	08.00	Quevy	157	Sat 18–5	40	35
Sun	19	May	07.00	Pont St Max	313	Fri 17–5	60	35
Sun	26	May	07.00	Noyon	271	Sat 25–5	60	35
Sat	1	Jun	06.00	Moulins	565	Thu30–5	125	35
Sun	2	Jun	06.00	Pont St Max	313	Sat 1–6	60	35
Sun	9	Jun	06.00	Melun	380	Sat 8–6	60	35

Dutch programme

Belgian programme

Race programme

There are great differences between the average Dutch and Belgian race programmes. As a result of a high degree of specialisation, the Belgians are able to put their birds into hampers every week for short distances from such places as Quievrain and Noyon, for the middle distances from Dourdan, Etampes and elsewhere, as well as for the long-distance races. The Dutch race programme is characterised by a phased build-up from short to longer distances.

Sprint, middle distance, long distance

The distances which racing pigeons have to cover vary widely, but this does not mean that they are entered one week for the short distances and the next week for the long distances. The purpose of specialization is precisely to exploit the build and temperament, sprint start or steady wing beat of the individual pigeon in the type of race that suits it best. The age of the pigeons plays a part, but so also does the preference of the fancier and he will direct his breeding accordingly.

Apart from the training flights which are held close to home or a little farther away, we distinguish three categories for the 'real'

work: sprint, middle distance and long distance.

Sprint races are over distances from 60 to 250 or 300 kilometres. The birds entered for these races are the explosive ones who diverge little from a straight line. The flight speed of the whole convoy is often roughly uniform. With this category, which is particularly popular in Belgium, what count most are cunning and speed in entering the loft.

Middle distance covers the distances between 300 and 500 kilometres. These races appeal to many fanciers partly for practical reasons. They are able to see the

	ANGOULEME	BARCELONA	BERGERAC	BORDEAUX	BOURGES	BRETEUIL	BRIVE	CAHORS	CHÂTEAUROUX	CLERMONT	COMPIEGNE	CORBEIL	CREIL	DAX	LAON	LA SOUTERRAINE	LIMOGES	LOURDES
ANTWERPEN	692	1103	768	801	483	365	708	807	529	248	230	321	257	930	192	595	643	963
GENT	652	1075	730	759	450	316	674	770	492	205	190	283	215	889	163	558	606	926
BRUSSEL	653	1060	727	762	310	441	332	666	766	488	212	191	281	220	150	554	602	922
CHARLEROI	617	1016	688	726	401	310	625	727	449	185	161	246	191	853	112	514	562	882
HASSELT	700	1085	769	809	479	394	702	807	530	270	246	329	276	935	195	595	643	961
LIEGE	683	1058	749	792	459	391	681	787	512	265	239	317	269	918	184	576	623	940
NAMUR	638	1027	707	747	418	338	642	746	469	212	187	268	217	874	134	533	581	900
LEEUWARDEN	932	1338	1008	1040	723	594	947	1047	769	485	469	561	495	1169	432	835	883	1203
AMSTERDAM	820	1233	897	927	613	482	838	936	658	373	357	449	383	1057	322	724	772	1092
WAGENINGEN	808	1203	881	917	593	485	817	920	641	367	347	436	375	1045	304	707	755	1074
ROOSENDAAL	725	1138	801	833	518	393	742	841	562	279	262	354	289	962	227	629	677	997
BOULOGNE	572	1035	660	674	408	215	619	701	434	159	169	242	173	804	192	499	544	856
LILLE	595	1029	675	702	400	255	622	716	439	148	138	230	160	832	126	505	553	872
SOUTHAMPTON	595	1091	691	679	509	286	678	730	509	324	346	380	334	801	389	563	599	875
DOVER	614	1082	703	714	457	257	666	744	481	210	219	292	224	844	239	545	589	899
LONDON	649	1135	743	742	525	307	717	783	538	299	315	373	312	868	344	598	639	934

pigeons arriving very nicely one at a time without a whole day being lost before it is all over.

The mile devourers among the pigeons are entered for the long distance races, which cover distances from 500 to as much as 1350 kilometres. Once a fancier has notched up a good long distance performance, he sometimes becomes attached to this category. Character, suppleness and endurance are the most obvious qualities which the birds need to possess for this 'heavy labour'.

Apart from the one-day long distance races up to about 800 kilometres, there are the overnight races. The pigeons are liberated at a time which makes it impossible for them to reach the home loft during the first day of the race.

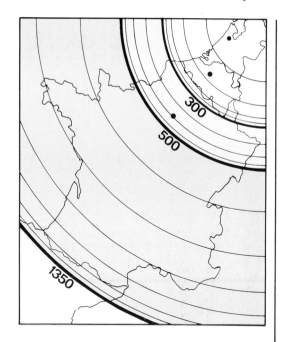

MARSEILLE	MEAUX	MELUN	MONTAUBAN	NOYON	ORLEANS	PAU	POITIERS	PONT-ST-MAX.	QUEVY	QUIEVRAIN	RIBECOURT	RUFFEC	ST-GHISLAIN	ST-QUENTIN	ST-VINCENT	SOISSONS	SURVILLIERS	TOURY	TOURS	VERVINS
883	273	324	833	208	411	951	596	249	101	103	217	655		172	945	218	269	381	505	158
869	237	288	800	169	372	913	553	208	76	69	178	613		135	903	185	229	341	461	134
841	232	283	791	169	372	910	557	211	60	66	179	616		133	905	177	231	341	467	115
794	196	246	750	139	336	872	524	181	37	54	149	581		105	869	140	199	307	435	75
849	280	329	826	224	419	952	607	266	117	130	234	664		189	952	224	284	391	520	159
815	268	315	802	219	405	932	594	259	121	137	228	648		186	935	213	275	379	508	149
798	219	268	765	166	358	890	546	207	67	84	175	602		132	890	163	224	330	459	98
1101	513	564	1073	447	651	1191	834	487	341	342	456	893	335	412	1183	458	509	620	742	397
1007	402	453	964	335	539	1080	721	375	231	231	345	781	224	300	1071	348	397	508	629	288
964	387	438	941	325	527	1064	713	367	215	221	335	771	213	289	1061	331	387	497	623	267
918	307	358	868	241	444	985	628	281	135	136	250	687	129	205	977	252	302	413	536	193
872	215	254	745	160	314	838	469	173			163	531		153	816	193	193	287	377	191
835	188	237	749	119	318	858	496	154			127	556		90	846	142	176	285	403	109
990	378	396	795	348	413	851	499	340			346	556		355	808	380	351	398	422	398
923	266	305	791	210	362	880	511	224			213	573		200	855	242	244	328	419	234
1002	357	387	840	310	427	912	548	315			311	609		305	877	342	331	403	462	343

Barcelona

The dream of every long-distance racer is to achieve a top performance at Barcelona. There is no possible argument about this . . . and it is not, in the first place, because of the 'big' money which is awarded to winners there. Just to gain a place is sufficient to catch the imagination and is a reason for calling such a prize winner 'Don Barcelona'.

The Sultan (ring number 6602176–81), best Belgian middle-distance pigeon, 'member' of the sport class team which was sent to the 1985 Olympiade at Oporto in Portugal.

Young Felix (3160054–80), first national Pau, Belgium, 1985.

NL80–1033490: best high-speed pigeon of the Netherlands in 1982.

The B81–3281380: first International Barcelona.

The fastest pigeon at Barcelona, 1985 (17,060 pigeons), but unfortunately it did not gain the international double: NL83–268430.

In 1984 this NL83–1774007 was the best Dutch middle-distance pigeon.

Background to the races

Homing ability, form and motivation are the three major characteristics which play a part in the success or otherwise of the race. The fancier does have means at his disposal to influence form and motivation, but homing ability, which enables the pigeons to find their way to the home loft, is something beyond his control, if only because nobody, not even scientists, yet knows precisely how it works.

Homing ability

How do pigeons find their way home? This is the key question of the sport. And we do not know the answer. At least we do not know precisely and certainly not on a sufficiently scientific basis. It is clear, in any event, that the pigeons not only orientate themselves, that is know where they are, but are also able to determine and stay on course to the home loft. They must therefore be able to navigate. Thus we prefer to speak of 'navigation ability', but as always we have chosen the most usual designation for introducing the subject.

Scientifically established navigation possibilities are the solar compass and the magnetic compass. The first 'instrument' is based on seeing the sun. Thanks to an internal clock, the pigeon is able to determine the location of a place with reference to the position of the sun at every moment of the day.

With the magnetic compass the pigeon finds its way home making use of the earth's magnetic field. This enables it to remain on course even with a completely overcast sky and hence in the absence of the sun's rays as an orientation point.

In addition, a number of theories are being investigated, of which we shall name a few. Sensitivity to slight changes in barometric pressure, which enable the air traveller to seek out the most favourable air layer. The possibility of observing polarized light, which, like the magnetic compass, is a useful aid when flying with an overcast sky. The penetration of ultra-violet light to the pigeon's retina, although it is not yet clear whether this light is used. The ability to pick up atmospheric sounds with a very low wave length, generated, for example, by earthquakes and magnetic storms. The role of the sense of smell.

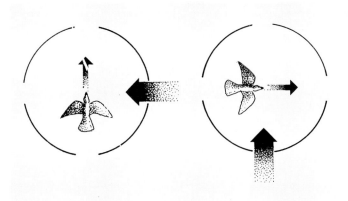

A diagrammatic impression of the operation of the solar compass. As the sun rotates so does the bird. With night flying the stars take the place of the sun.

SUNLIGHT

DIRECTION OF FLIGHT

The pigeons pictured here, who spend the whole day in an open aviary, are very healthy but they are not really on form.

Form

Athletes on form are able to achieve outstanding performances: better performances than their fellows, who may be equally fast, but are not on form; better results than they themselves achieved a month ago or may achieve in two weeks' time. Form cannot be measured and is therefore the subject of a lot of myths – and of playing on the fancier's uncertainty when that kind of nonsense is offered as a criterion of form at ridiculous prizes. A good fancier laughs at all this; he knows and feels when his birds are on form. And he has done all he can. He has provided the correct food and rest. He has provided the basic precondition of good housing and has had the help of the sun's rays. Because form is not just health; it is the result, the sum total, of the best possible accommodation, care, food, management and correct training.

The aim should, of course, be to maintain form over a long period, but it is impossible to prevent the occurrence of a curve with marked peaks indicating top form when the birds seem to be capable of everything. They are in splendid physical and mental equilibrium and unbeatable.

With widowers, form is partly determined by the sex hormones. The level of performance among sexually mature young pigeons will be enhanced by a good scratch for food. Nesting pigeons experience strong fluctuations in this respect, depending upon the stage of development of the nest. This demonstrates the importance of good record-keeping. By recording the dates of peak form in one year we shall certainly benefit in the following years.

The 'weighing' of form

Being mobile and eager to fly, mischievous, pugnacious, bent on expanding its territory – these are all forms of behaviour which the observant fancier likes to see. His pigeons are on good form. Moreover, with the pigeon in his hand the fancier can feel other physical characteristics than those just described: the bird appears lighter, it is puffed up and round; the pectoral muscles are lightly stretched and he feels a vibration. The skin around the breastbone is smooth and stretched; the flesh is pink to red (not bluish). A nesting pigeon feels distinctly sweaty, as does a widower who has been in the basket for a little while. Red, preferably rather warm-feeling legs without scurf are characteristic of pace-setting pigeons.

Sunday suit

The plumage of pigeons on form may be compared with a Sunday suit. Everything is perfectly in place, not a feather is out of place. The cover feathers under the flights are neatly arranged in roof-tile fashion. The gloss on the plumage – although here the simile no longer applies – tells the fancier that he need have no worries. Characteristics of a pigeon on form are dry shining eyes, chalky white beak wattles (with the exception of birds which are nursing young) and white eye ceres (although not with colours which depart from nature).

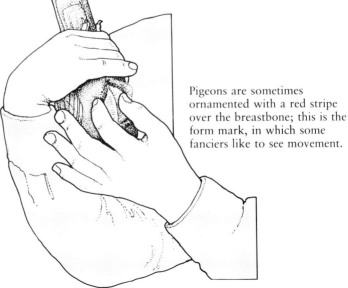

Pigeons are sometimes ornamented with a red stripe over the breastbone; this is the form mark, in which some fanciers like to see movement.

Motivation

Every average racing pigeon has it in itself to fly home from the liberation point. If it does not succeed the cause is probably an accident, sickness, severe atmospheric disturbance etc. But the fancier is not just concerned with the ability to fly in the direction of the loft. The bird must fly quickly, via the shortest route and, preferably, ahead of the opposition. Fanciers strive, some rather more earnestly than others, to have a winning pigeon and preferably one that is a winner in a wider context.

It is logical that the pigeon must be motivated in order for it to give of its very best. There seem to be scarcely any limits to owners' ingenuity when it comes to increasing that motivation. The following are some examples of their tricks. A pot egg with a bluebottle; a piece of string is clamped between the two halves of a pot egg and the fancier regularly pulls at the string so that the pigeon is constantly engaged in getting the egg under itself. Placing bantam eggs which are about to hatch under the mother pigeon; she has the greatest trouble in keeping the young under her. Letting the hen see her own cock paying court to another hen. Increasing the number of eggs to five or six. Separating a hen from her young, stuffing her with food, then bringing the two together again and placing them in the basket at the moment of feeding. A flight between the pigeon to be placed in the basket, the certain winner, and the owner of a nesting compartment where she found the strange company on her return.

This is only a selection: everyone plays the game in his own way. We must be careful that tricks do not rebound on us and result in demotivation, or that they are completely lacking in respect for animal life. Working with special feeding or treats will certainly serve the purpose. For the rest, experience will teach how far one can go before the pigeons no longer respond.

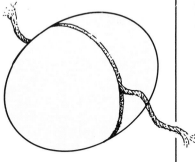

Even the ticking of an alarm clock can give the pigeon the idea that there are eggs about to hatch and so increase the urge to reach the nest.

A pot egg manipulated with the aid of a piece of string is only one of the 'tricks' employed to increase motivation.

Techniques of the sport

On the following pages we shall look at the ways of playing the sport, including not only well-used methods such as the widowhood system but also some less frequently used ones. A striking feature of these methods is that they are often based on jealousy and the urge to reach the nest. They therefore form a practical supplement to the theory of motivation.

Form characteristics on the wing

The training of widowers in progress. This provides another opportunity to observe which pigeons are on form. Observe how the convoy of birds spreads out and then joins up again. Observe how they alight on the roof and take off again. Observe not only a sky full of movement but also the solitary dreamer on a chimney who repeatedly re-enters the loft for an inspection. Note also how some birds separate themselves from the group to chase after strange pigeons.

Widowhood

As we approach the end of the book we should like to remark how the multiplicity of topics to be covered occasionally makes our task more difficult. The widowhood system is *the* technique for many fanciers. The system is based on sexual attraction and avoiding having to bring up young pigeons, with its taxing demands on the parent birds' strength. An important condition for success is allowing the birds to rest between two bursts of effort. This maintains the form at a constant level.

As the name of the system indicates, cocks and hens live apart. During the week the hens remain with other hens in the run or in a separate compartment. The cocks train for half an hour or an hour twice a day and then rest. (Obscure the light, if necessary, with curtains or lime wash on the glass and do not disturb them further.) Immediately before the cocks are placed in the baskets the cocks and hens are put together in their nesting bowls for a couple of minutes. Most of those who use the widowhood system consider that courting is enough, it need not go so far as mating. The cocks which are leaving go in the basket, those who stay behind must leave the loft.

When the cocks return home they can remain longer with their hens, from half an hour to half a day, depending on how strenuous the race has been. The fancier must learn the most appropriate period by trial and error. After being shown the hen a few times experienced cocks already know from the mere turning over of the nesting bowl what the intention is.

In recent years there has been an increased interest in playing the widowhood system with hens, and fanciers have even been successful with total widowhood in which both the cock and the hen have to race. The great advantage is that they can participate in the sport with more birds at the same time. The disadvantage of there being no partner when the bird returns home can be overcome by providing a warm reception with a replacement. The majority of pigeons are not so shy. A further disadvantage is that if a cock and a hen arrive back from a race at the same time they have more interest in each other than in the loft so that precious minutes are lost.

Widowers' loft

The nesting compartments must be so constructed that the hens can be shut up in them but also so that part is available to the cock. The hen will be waiting after the race, the cock flies into his nesting compartment and can easily be picked up. The nest bowl is reversed during the week or replaced by a block of wood.

Showing

Immediately before the race the hen is briefly left with the cock. This is called 'showing'. When the pair are cooing in the nest bowl it is time to put the cock in the basket. This is the practice mainly among those who enter birds for the sprint and middle-distance races. Some fanciers, notably those who participate in long-distance races, see no objection to the cock mating with the hen under these circumstances. They sometimes allow the pair to stay together for up to half a day.

Obligatory rest

Without rest and sleep a widower achieves less than he is capable of. Lying on his side between races, he should have to worry about nothing. This is beneficial to his condition. Rest in the loft can be increased by whitewashing the windows or by fitting frosted glass, so that widowers are not aroused by every pigeon that flies past. The advantage of shielding the windows with curtains is that the sun's rays can be allowed into the loft at any time we choose. There is no need to worry about regularly recurring sounds, even quite loud ones, the birds soon become accustomed to them. And you cannot protect them against the boom of a jet fighter breaking the sound barrier.

The birds need to rest between races. Roller or slatted blinds enable us to regulate the amount of sun entering the loft.

The natural system

This system is so called because it makes use of natural possibilities and exploits the most advantageous times for the races. Only experience can teach us the best times because they differ for each bird (good record-keeping helps here!). The general rule are: race nesting hens sitting on eggs, on eggs about to hatch and on squeakers up to 12 days old; nesting cocks produce the best performances on sitting on squeakers of ten days and older, on young in the nest and sitting and on driving.

Hens seldom deliver outstanding performances on young (one to five days). However, it is just in this situation that the females produce wins on the overnight long-distance events! It must be said that champion pigeons win prizes in all conditions, but it is wicked to put hens who are due to lay into the baskets.

Spaciously constructed nesting compartments, with room for two nest bowls, invite the pigeons to lay a second brood. They do this much earlier with a spacious arrangement such as the one shown in the photograph. There are already young in the bowl, top right, while the parents are busy with the second nest on the left.

Use of a partition

If design provision has been made for this, the partition can be replaced by a wire blind as the day approaches for putting the birds into the baskets, after which the nest bowls of two pairs are brought closer together. The jealousy thus aroused and the threatening behaviour on both sides increase the motivation. We can go still further by removing the blind and allowing the pigeons to fight over a single nest bowl (possibly with pot eggs). This method should be considered only if they are remaining in the basket for a short time.

Mirror flight

Using a mirror produces the same effect as removing the partition. If the bowl is moved increasingly closer to the mirror the pigeon begins to fight and strike at itself. This is a strong incentive for it to have a tussle with the intruder immediately after the return home.

Sense of duty

A hen with young does not really need any additional motivation to set course for the spot where her squeakers are waiting. The presence of the young birds is often sufficient in itself for her to produce a prize-winning performance.

Cotes and the bully

One of the forms of the sport which is based on jealousy and aggression is the cote system. In this very interesting and varied technique each pair has its own little loft, in which family life goes on without the family being troubled by peeping toms. When the time arrives for putting the birds in the baskets, the cock which is to go in the basket is shut out and at the same time the fancier places a very conspicuous rival, the bully, in the cote. The intruder must be not only pugnacious but also sexually excited so that he immediately goes for the hen or at least makes an attack on the nest. The legitimate occupant of the cote is forced to watch impotently while the stranger takes up and sweeps the floor with everything he holds dear. When the cote owner has worked himself up sufficiently, the fancier allows him into the cote for a moment. It is easy to guess what happens. The cocks attack each other, but before too many feathers fly the fancier intervenes again. He places the husband in the basket and removes the bully from the cote.

With the cote system, coming in after the race presents no problem. After a few times, simply showing the bully is sufficient to rouse the ire of the cote 'owner'. This system, which was once very popular among Belgian sprint racers, is no longer much practised and is suitable only for very short distances with a short stay in the basket.

A typical tiled roof with some cotes. They form the entrances to an equal number of racing pigeon family homes. Up until World War II the cote system was in regular use among Belgian fanciers who concentrated on the short distances, whether or not in combination with other systems. The system is now little used.

The cote system is incomplete without the bully. This conspicuous fellow arouses the greatest possible jealousy in the rightful inhabitant of the cote, without necessarily going so far as to mate with the hen. The latter's paying court to the intruder, while the husband looks on without being able to intervene, is in itself sufficient motivation for him to complete the return flight from the liberation point at the greatest possible speed.

In the service of the sport

Before the sometimes tens of thousands of racing pigeons are in the air, a lot of people have done a great deal of work. There are lots of practical things to be done before the modern racing pigeon 'business', as this gigantic flying operation might well be called, is working efficiently. The following pages deal with baskets, clocks and means of transport, as well as with training and registration, so they are partly about pigeons and their owners. But they have everything to do with the subject.

Training

Winning performances necessitate training. This applies as much to pigeons as to sportsmen. The preparations for the racing season begin after the winter rest. With the arrival of spring the activity of hormones spontaneously increases the desire to fly. Variation in the diet stimulates the flying urge still further. Set training periods are needed to establish the desired rhythm.

Nesting pigeons are removed from the nest and obliged to join in the training sessions, but the urge to return to the bowl is too strong. Fanciers with an open loft will see that they quickly go in.

Shutting them out is one way to prevent this. Nesting pigeons will eventually see that their efforts to get in are fruitless. We can also decide to let out the pigeons which are not on 'nest duty', which means the cocks in the mornings and evenings and the hens in the middle of the day.

Shutting out

Training widowers with closed flaps is no better than with an open loft. For the fancier who has other things to do in the mornings, shutting the birds out is obviously more practical. After half an hour the door is opened, the flock is allowed to storm in after a single call and the fancier can go off to work with an easy heart. He can then train in the evening with an open loft. It is a pleasure to see the widowers flying in and out and inspecting the loft. At the same time the fancier can get some idea of their form.

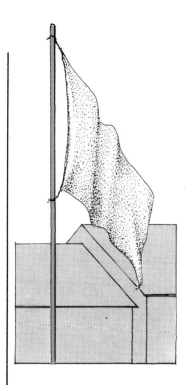

Flagging

Human intervention is also required to provide extra discipline during racing pigeon training. By placing a flag on the loft, for example, the training period can be increased from 10 to 45 minutes. At first some chasing will have to be done to prevent the birds perching calmly next to the flag. Remember that exaggeration does more harm than good and flagging is not universal. Some fanciers go still farther by placing a stuffed bird on the flap. Whether the birds which are treated in this way come in when they have to is the question. The answer depends largely on the calibre of the fancier.

Cycling fanciers sometimes have to execute great feats of balancing skill on the way to the club house . . .

Line of flight

Training flights around the house are only a means of exercising the pigeons' muscles. They also have to become accustomed to the race rhythm, to endurance. This occurs during line-of-flight training, which is done on a club basis. Many a fancier becomes restless, however, with the approach of the racing season and sets off for the south himself with the baskets in the car.

Sprint specialists, but others also, prefer to release the pigeons singly. This strengthens the birds' self-confidence and trains them particularly in the almost blind flying of the last part of the course. For young pigeons in particular this thorough training is useful for when they have to make an all-out effort in the months ahead. The raising of the distance in jumps of from five to ten kilometres after a first short flight close to home presents no difficulty to the young guard. For old, experienced pigeons greater jumps are acceptable.

Pool form

The race registration or entry form contains the necessary information to enable a ranking of the competing pigeons to be made. Besides the data about the participant, including the distance to the loft or the coordinates, there are the pigeons' ring numbers. It is customary to enter the competing birds on the form in the order in which they are expected home. As a check, the club enters the numbers of the race rings used and collects the stake data from all the participants. The entry forms are still far from standardized, although there has been some improvement in response to computer processing.

Although the sport of pigeon racing and betting on it are two separate things, the gambling element – however modest – gives a great many pigeon fanciers an extra dimension to their hobby. Relations, friends, colleagues, many people, occasionally place a bet. With special races there may be quite exceptional prizes such as a car. We should incidentally not omit to mention that, particularly in the Netherlands, special charity and youth sweeps are organized in association with national and other major events, the proceeds of which are donated to the respective causes.

Filling in

The entry form must be carefully filled in. This is best done at home. The order in which the pigeons are entered may be important for winning the championships, but the position on the form may also be important as far as the betting is concerned.

Belgian entry forms

Belgium/The Netherlands

In Belgium there are many different possibilities, from 1:4 to 'has who has', i.e. everything in one throw. The number of stakes placed indicates to which pigeons they apply. E.g. placed three times up to Bfr.500 applies to the first, second and third entered (position on the entry form). Taking part in the pools is a well-known pastime here. Money is paid out on four times and eight times the stake, respectively. In the Netherlands it is usual to place a cross against the names of the birds one is betting on. In other words, one can place a higher stake against the fifth marked bird than against the first.

MIDFONDCLUB OOST-BRABANT																							
Vereniging:								Te:															
Lid Midfondclub				ja nee			Rayon			1		2		3		4							
ALLE POELEN MET „X" INVULLEN										LIDNUMMER:													
1:4							1:10		1:25				SPECIALE POELEN										
tnng	25	50	75	100	150	250	500	100	150	100	200	H.W.H.	Spec.	Kon.	H1	H2	S3	S4	Derby	MF.			
	1	2	3	4	5	6	7	1	2	1	2									X			
	1	2	3	4	5	6	7	1	2	1	2									X			
	1	2	3	4	5	6	7	1	2	1	2									X			
	1	2	3	4	5	6	7	1	2	1	2									X			
	1	2	3	4	5	6	7	1	2	1	2									X			
	1	2	3	4	5	6	7	1	2	1	2									X			
	1	2	3	4	5	6	7	1	2	1	2									X			
	1	2	3	4	5	6	7	1	2	1	2									X			
	1	2	3	4	5	6	7	1	2	1	2									X			
	1	2	3	4	5	6	7	1	2	1	2									X			
	1	2	3	4	5	6	7	1	2	1	2									X			
	1	2	3	4	5	6	7	1	2	1	2									X			
	1	2	3	4	5	6	7	1	2	1	2									X			

Detail of Dutch form

Basket

Pigeons are placed in baskets or hampers for transport to the club house and to the liberation point for the training flights. Many kinds of basket are available in the trade. In order to save money, it is worth considering what we can make using our own skill.

Good baskets and hampers should meet the following conditions: they must be firm, not too large and not too heavy (particularly important with DIY) and provided with sufficient ventilation. They have a thick bottom and raised sides, so that the interior of the car is not dirtied more than is strictly necessary. They have a partition to separate the sexes and an outer *and* inner lid to prevent escaping.

Don't forget about regular cleaning.

Formerly only reed or osier baskets were available for transporting pigeons to where they were put into hampers. One still occasionally sees them being made at craft fairs.

Between 1 and 16 compartments

There are travelling baskets with a single compartment, but there are also outsize ones with from 12 to 16 (2 × 8) compartments. It is very handy, in any event, to have a small hamper available, for picking up a single stray bird for example.

Reeds

We no longer often see baskets made from real woven reeds or osiers. The quality of the modern article sometimes leaves much to be desired.

Compartmented basket

This prevents the pigeons attacking each other. Fights do occur in the large travelling basket of course but there the possibilities of flight are greater. Placing the birds in a compartmented basket has the additional advantage that they can be removed in the order in which they appear on the entry form. Compartments with doors on the front are not recommended. The best type are those which are loaded from the top. Removable partitions make it possible to load more pigeons if required.

Woven reed baskets exist for transporting pigeons to the liberation point by train or by ordinary lorry, while there are aluminium baskets for use in special pigeon containers.

Wood

With a wooden basket pay attention to the weight. A wooden carrier is generally very solid, but this should not be at the expense of manoeuvrability.

Aluminium

This is a particularly suitable material for pigeon baskets. As it is impermeable, particular attention should be paid to ventilation.

The floor of the basket

The most desirable floor covering for baskets are wood shavings (left), in which the droppings are immediately absorbed. A disadvantage is the pollution of the liberation site. One of the tasks of clubs is to leave these places tidy after them. An alternative is corrugated cardboard. It is satisfactory for a short stay in the basket, but soon becomes a sticky mess after a few nights in the basket. A number of clubs are very enthusiastic about special meshes which reduce the danger of infection.

Lastly, there are now special mats on the market.

Space

The pigeons must not be crammed into the travelling basket. The latter must be so arranged that the sexes can be segregated.

Clock

The race ring is only one half of the system for checking the course of the races. The other half consists of the clock, which has a certificate of approval from the league. They are quite expensive. (If every fancier was totally honest and did not deduct a second from the time at which a pigeon entered the loft, costs would be considerably reduced!) But the reality is different. Moreover, organizing competitions would be very impractical without clocks, especially for short races where pigeons competing in different races arrive at the same time.

In earlier days the fancier or his representative had to run as fast as he could to the club room, originally with the pigeon and later with just a rubber ring. Now every fancier owns one or more clocks which record the time when the race ring is fed onto the pinion, the ring wheel. A number of security devices prevent cheating. The best known of these is the spike. The locking mechanism ensures that a hole is punched at the beginning and end of the paper tape which runs with the clock. Any premature opening of the clock causes a hole to be punched which should not be there.

Types of clock

There is a wide range of mechanical clocks, quartz clocks, and computer clocks for linking with peripherals.

Clock committee

Before the fancier can use his clock a committee sets and starts it. It 'regulates' the clock, according to the jargon. This is an extremely important task because errors may mean exclusion from the competition. The clocks are started at the same time and, as we shall see, pass through the control after the race.

In Belgium the race ring has first to be placed in a cylinder before the fancier can clock in.

Ringing/putting into baskets

The pigeons taking part in a race have to record a result at sometimes hundreds of kilometres from each other. This is quite different from a combined arrival at a stadium or two sportsmen competing against each other on the track or road. The sporting sucess of a pigeon race stands or falls, therefore, with a watertight control. Adding a financial aspect to the sporting one only makes such a control all the more necessary.

The basis of the control system is a rubber ring with a number. On the inside of the ring are printed a serial letter, a number and a year. This data and the different colours of the rings ensure that no two pigeons have the same ring. The ring is put onto the pigeon's leg when it goes into the basket at the beginning of the race. All the numbers of the sometimes thousands of pigeons in a race are recorded. A recapitulation table is made of the total number of pigeons despatched. The table also includes the stakes which have been placed, so that the fancier cannot alter his stake form after the event. Today many of them are entered in a computer.

The race ring bears the number and on the inside the serial letter and number, and year of issue.

In Belgium the latter three elements are often replaced by the club name.

Strips of 25 rubber race rings, including the numbers. The participants' stubs are sorted and kept by the fancier after the birds have been put into the baskets.

Belgian 'Derby ring', used in competing for a separate prize comprising the proceeds from the sale of the rings.

The ring is put on with ingenious devices such as the one shown here. The 'claws' open, the ring is stretched, the bird's leg is inserted into the apparatus and the ring is drawn over the leg. And now let us hope that the pigeon quickly returns home with the ring.

Transport

The owner has entrusted his pigeon to the care of others. A counting mechanism is often fitted to the door to warn the conveyor when the crate is full.

After the preparations in the club room have been completed, the first part of the journey begins. The pigeons do not have to do anything. The baskets are taken by various means of transport to the liberation point. The care of the birds is taken over from the fanciers by the conveyors, people who undoubtedly have a very responsible task in accompanying their precious cargo. In earlier days the conveyors were the people who provided the first pigeon transport of modern times, at first carrying a pigeon basket on their backs and then by horse and cart.

In Great Britain there has been a big increase in road transport since British Rail deliberately priced pigeons off its rolling stock. The Fancy has invested heavily in the specially designed road transporters carrying as many as 6,000 birds which can be simultaneously released by the conveyor at the liberation point.

Transport in Belgium is still largely dependent on private contractors. Many reed baskets are still used, being loaded into ordinary lorries. Transport by train is still employed for races from beyond Paris. The train transport in Barcelona is well known, with the feathered travellers being cared for in relaxed and spacious conditions.

Aircraft

As early as 1922 a cargo aircraft was specially fitted out for pigeon transport. Use was later made of this form of transport by the long-distance race organizers. The speed of the aircraft and the resulting reduction in the number of nights spent in the basket (the longer the time spent on the journey, the greater the chance that the birds will be off form) cannot be praised enough, but the gain in time is often largely offset by the distance to the airport. The high costs also mean that aircraft are not a viable form of pigeon transport.

Containers provide first-class amenities for the pigeons: air conditioning, water supply, space for looking after them.

At the rear you see the door which enables the conveyor to reach all the pigeons. It is important that the interior should be level so that the water stays in the drinking troughs.

Lorry

Transporting racing pigeons by ordinary lorry makes it possible to place the baskets outside the lorry so that the pigeons can all be started off from the same side. This is seen as an advantage in comparison with the container which does not have this possibility. A disappointing race result is often blamed on the position of the baskets at the top or bottom in the row.

The moment of truth

In the following pages we follow the pigeons through the race itself. These are the hours between liberation and their landing on the platform. While their owners anxiously await reports from foreign parts, the pigeons have to prove their sporting worth. Now nothing can be altered, no more adjustments can be made. The birds will have to set their compasses on the correct course themselves, avoid their enemies and brave any deteriorating weather conditions.

Not one human being has yet participated in their race from beginning to end.

Liberation

From the moment the pigeons take off into the air, the full responsibility for their wellbeing lies with someone else, so it has to be an experienced man who entrusts our birds to the elements. He needs to have a good relationship with the people and bodies who provide information about the weather (this aspect is dealt with later) and with the conveyors on the spot. Another requirement of the liberators is that they should release all the pigeons as far as possible at the same time. The pigeon container is a great advance in this respect. A liberation site must also be free of all obstacles such as wires and trees. The aim of all these requirements is to give all the birds the same chance.

The pigeons are on the way to what is their and our moment of truth. In the club room the clocks are synchronized with the radio time signal or the master clock. The same operation is repeated when the clocks are brought in. Obviously, the chance of being ahead or behind is greater as the distance increases. Differences between clocks must be adjusted in the interests of a fair contest.

Awaiting the signal

Rain and fog are conditions under which no one will give the starting signal. The pigeons wait on the ground in hope of better weather.

Liberation from transporters

With liberation from a transporter the pigeons start off almost simultaneously through the doors on the right- and left-hand sides of the vehicle. There are two main systems. The first works by means of flaps which spring open simultaneously when a handle is operated . . . at least if the mechanism is properly maintained. In the second system the baskets are provided with half escape openings. One half is kept closed until the moment of release, while the basket is already open. The birds are able to leave when the other half is also opened.

The starting signal

The siren has sounded. The starting signal has been given. The pigeons take to the air in their thousands practically all at the same time. Depending on the weather conditions, their form and experience, they first make some exploratory rounds before setting out on course for home. Fanciers are becoming increasingly convinced that it is not only the pigeon's speed which forms an important element in a successful race, but also the ability to set a straight course for home.

The conveyors open the reed or cane baskets by pulling open the doors. They do so starting at the bottom.

Line of flight/routes

The pigeons have been given their freedom. Now they set out for home with the aid of their navigation system and affected by the weather conditions. The route between the liberation point and home is called the line of flight. The commonest direction [for the Low Countries] is from southwest to northeast, but this is not essential as far as orientation is concerned. Although the races which catch the imagination are the ones along the southwest–northeast line, there is also an interest in races from West Germany (including Munich), Great Britain (Parkstone) and the North Netherlands (Roodeschool).

The result is determined by the route which the birds choose. They fly around natural obstacles such as mountains and water. The coastline, motorways, rivers and valleys form part of the fixed route. It is striking how pigeons, as observations have proved, always pass the same points, either alone or in small groups. Towards the end of the flight they do so at a very low height. Landmarks in the vicinity probably do not play an important part. The race is not won in the last few miles. Nor can the pigeons then make up lost ground.

The wind force blows them off the straight course, which is why a high proportion of the prizes in a race from a number of points goes to the birds starting from the quarter from which the wind is blowing.

Both natural waterways and artificial canals form part of the route map of the airborne racers. On the last leg of the race landmarks in their own vicinity such as the tower of the village church play a part. The pigeons reconnoitre these during their line-of-flight training. Although the time saving is not great it does count, particularly in short-distance races.

Enemies

Their position in the food chain ensures that pigeons also have their natural enemies. On their journey through the air they are threatened by birds of prey (hawk, sparrowhawk, kestrel). It is difficult to feel respect for the natural laws which govern the struggle for existence in the animal world when our prize specimens become their victims.

Man himself may also be the cause of death and destruction among the racing pigeon population: agricultural pesticides, air pollution, as well as overhead power lines, aerials and . . . bridges. Our pigeons will also have evaded these perils before they can touch down on the home platform.

With the arrival of cable television and the use of the communal central aerial, the number of aerials has been visibly reduced. This is fortunate because pigeons have considerable difficulty in finding their way through such a steel jungle. They can also collide with numerous telephone and electricity cables. The leading pigeons in the team see the cables and suddenly rise. The following group cannot react until the last moment and run the risk of flying to their deaths or suffering more or less serious injuries. Placing spheres on the cables, which are visible from a distance, can partly reduce this risk. Buried cables are still better, or course.

A hawk

will attack pigeons, particularly during the winter. Over 30 rings were once found under a hawk's eyrie. As soon as other young birds are available, the hawks leave pigeons alone.

The weasel is another threat to the loft. The creature is able to get in through the smallest opening.

Fanciers have also thought up ingenious devices to counter the racing pigeon's flying enemies, such as this bird of prey whistle from Indonesia.

The weather

Weather conditions largely determine the course of the race. It's easy to criticize the liberators, but what is the reality? Liberating the birds in fine, open weather presents no problems, but where there is doubt the decision may have a better outcome on one occasion than on another. Moreover, there are fanciers and fanciers. One will say 'Let them go, let them go, my birds are ready for it', while another is more cautious and – in the eyes of the other fancier – keeps his pigeons wrapped in cotton wool. Some allowance should therefore be made for decisions which turn out to be wrong. Once the birds have been released there is no turning back.

The weather affects not only the pigeon's orientation and navigation and the straightness or otherwise of its course. Good fliers will also seek out those air layers which give them the most help. With a favourable wind they will fly high, where the wind is strongest. If there is a head wind they will fly low over the landscape, where the wind is not so strong and its force is broken by all kinds of obstacles.

Shallow cumulus such as this is a sign of good weather.

With this kind of cloud the wind is variable. Rapidly growing cumulus clouds usually bring rain. If the tops begin to curl upwards you may also expect strong winds.

Weather conditions as in the photograph above give cause to expect a favourable end to the race, at least as far as the weather is concerned. The cloud cover is open and the sun is visible. There will be no real navigation problems.

During a thunderstorm pigeons stay in or on the liberation point. The high electrical discharges can seriously affect their orientation. Sudden changes in air pressure associated with lightning strikes, violent precipitation accompanied by hail, and the sensation of fear also makes things difficult for the birds.

Below: A cumulo-nimbus cloud (on the left of the picture) which has produced a heavy shower may cause violent gusts of wind. The temperature will also fall. The sky will often clear at sunset.

Weather forecast

A good overview of the weather situation in Europe enables a considered decision to be made about releasing the birds. Through their 'delegates' at the start of the race fanciers today are able to enjoy the services of weather stations such as that of the Air Force. With great care and an increasing sense of what is important for a successful pigeon race, they try to forecast the weather to be expected along the line of flight. The forecasters work with extremely refined equipment for carrying out the complicated calculations at lightning speed and with a variety of means of communication, which keep them in touch with a large body of weather organizations throughout Western Europe. Unexpected freaks of nature can, of course, upset a carefully considered decision. Weathermen are the first to admit this.

Pigeon fanciers show a great interest in the weather forecasts. The decision whether or not to put the pigeons in the baskets is often taken after their owners have listened to the weather reports. It is as well, therefore, not to cast this expert advice to the winds.

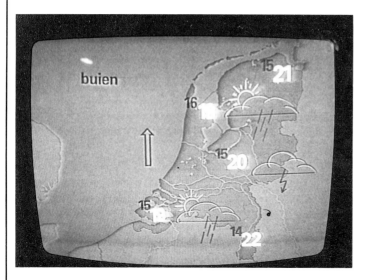

While the weather experts study satellite photographs, fanciers look worriedly or optimistically at their barometers, but the glass in a house at the liberation point may present a very different picture from that at the fancier's home.

Weather maps are shown every day after the television news. The forecasts cover more days than previously, although the necessary safety margin is built into the longer term predictions. The distribution of high and low pressure areas and other weather phenomena, even when photographed remotely from a satellite, may look very different after a few days. Constant adjustment has to be made for unexpected disturbances.

Fog/inversion

Not only thick fog but even patches of mist can mean navigation problems for our pigeons. As a precaution, liberation should not take place under these conditions. The conveyors have to wait until the fog lifts under the warming influence of the sun's rays. This is not to say that pigeons lose all sense of direction in fog. On the contrary, it has been proved that they don't by birds which safely reach the home platform even in particularly poor visibility.

Not every expert agrees that inversion has a fatal effect on race results leading to the loss of pigeons during the race. Whatever the truth, inversion is in ordinary language,

when a warm moist air layer is held trapped between colder layers. The effect of this is that air travellers observe the sun in a different position from where it really is. The phenomenon occurs quite suddenly.

Reference is being made increasingly in pigeon literature to the effect which disturbances of the sun may have on homing ability. This kind of natural phenomenon is also mentioned as a possible cause of bad finishes to races where the whole line of flight appears perfect.

Falling cold air

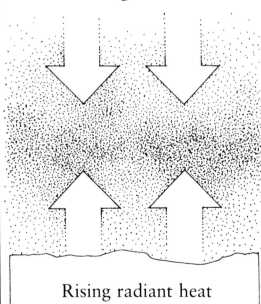

Rising radiant heat

Origin of fog

Relatively warm air can absorb a lot of moisture. In calm weather many small dust particles accumulate, greatly reducing the visibility in the moist and polluted air. When the air cools during the evening and night, the absorption of water vapour is reduced and fog forms.

How inversion occurs

The phenomenon of inversion illustrated diagrammatically. Dry cold air (3) and moist warm air (4) refract the sunlight. The sun (1) apparently lies in a different position (2). This means that a familiar object (5) appears to be in a different place (6).

Recording

An experienced fancier leaves a wide margin when calculating the time of arrival. He knows all too well how uncertain things can be *en route*. As he estimates his chances, he prepares the loft. He shuts up the non-fliers in the nesting compartment in the expectation that the pigeons will then be able to enter without hindrance from traps or crowding by the other birds. He provides fresh but not too cold water, possibly in separate vessels, and places the hen, if he is using the widowhood system, in its nest bowl.

When any early pigeon arrives many people hold their breath. Such a moment places a great strain on the nerves. If anything is said the arrival turns into a tormentor who hestitates about landing. And yet we have to get hold of the race ring; without the ring the time cannot be recorded. Some pigeons allow themselves to be picked up while they are still outside. This is the first step to independent clocking-on by the pigeon itself . . .

Control measures

Bodies which organize races may prescribe how recording is to be carried out and lay down time limits to eliminate any chance of cheating. At international level the pigeons are often given a secret mark (letter or number stamped on the wing) which must be entered on a form and clocked. There are rules which cannot be flouted. Breaking them leads to expulsion.

It is quite logical that cheating, which harms the reputation of the sport, should be punished, although it is hard that exceeding the time limit by a couple of seconds because of nerves on the part of an elderly fancier when a pigeon arrives unexpectedly early should have results in the loss of a big prize, certainly when the limit was later extended. This was an actual case in the Netherlands which was taken to the courts and fascinated the pigeon world.

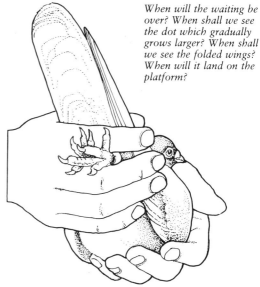

When will the waiting be over? When shall we see the dot which gradually grows larger? When shall we see the folded wings? When will it land on the platform?

In the hand

We must force ourselves to pick up the pigeon as calmly as possible. Widowers and nesting pigeons fly more readily into their nest compartment where they can be picked up, the race ring removed and the timing operation completed. Do not throw the pigeon back after this but release it gently. Young pigeons are picked up at the feeding trough from among a number of other birds. In the chapter on accommodation, systems such as the sputnik and the supertrap which can help us at this difficult moment have already been discussed.

Recording the time

Before we can use the clock for the purpose for which we have bought it, namely timing the pigeons, it must be within hand's reach. After picking up the pigeon we first remove the rubber ring. Depending upon the type of clock and the rules, the ring is first inserted in a thimble and then in the opening provided, after which the paper tape inside the clock is turned on with a key. This is the actual recording operation which is visible in the window.

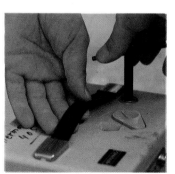

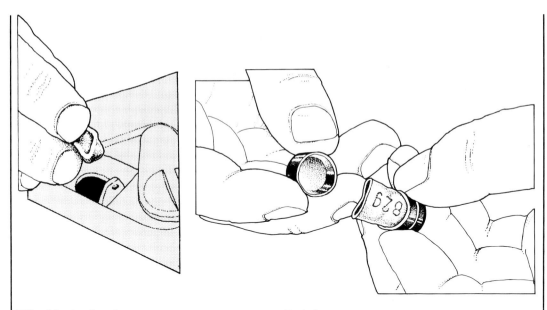

The Netherlands

The latest versions of pigeon clocks intended for the Netherlands are so constructed that the race ring can be inserted without using a thimble. The ring wheel is fitted with arms which catch the ring as it spins away. With national races it is obligatory to register a red ticket with the ring number of the clocked pigeon within three minutes of the two race rings, one of which is a control ring. The fancier can take his own precautions by inserting the second ring in a control clock. The second clock then counts if the first one should prove faulty.

Belgium

In Belgium it is obligatory to place the ring in a thimble, cylinder, tube or clamp before registering it. This makes it impossible to tamper with the ring afterwards, such as by first registering and then working in the ring in some devious manner. The Belgians are not convinced of the security of the Dutch system, so that at national and other important competitions it is also obligatory to insert the second race ring in a control clock.

Sealing

After the mechanism, paper tape and ring wheel have been set, the clock is closed with the aid of a device which, as has already been described, punches a hole in the paper tape. The clock is also sealed as a precaution against unauthorized opening. The seal, of tin, is more a safeguard against accidental opening than a watertight system of sealing.

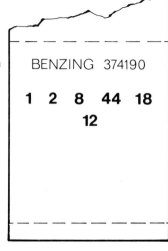

BENZING 374190

1 2 8 44 18
12

Paper printout

A printout on the paper tape (left) taken from a very modern type of clock:
Benzing 374190 (clock number which is printed with every record)
- 1 (indicates the receptacle number)
- 2 (indicates the number of days after punching)
- 8 (number of hours)
- 44 (number of minutes
- 18 (number of seconds
Thus a pigeon which arrives six seconds later gets the following printout:
Benzing 374190
2 2 8 44 24

Lost pigeons

After the young guard have been trained and are accustomed to being outside, sleepless nights await those fanciers whose colony is halved from one day to the next. They have a splendid young team, healthy, eager to fly and then they are gone . . . The odd one returns home, thin, exhausted and bewildered, but where are the others?

Pigeons also stay behind on races, and often not the worst ones. Daily inspection of the loft in search of the favourite sometimes produces a 'stranger in the house'. Examples are known of pigeons returning years later. Such a lost son or daughter is received with awe, but often there is nothing to do but hope.

Central lofts

Pigeons which are picked up may be given a place in a central loft. The manager is responsible for reporting the find, for which he receives a modest fee (which scarcely compensates for the trouble and the sometimes unreasonable comments of the owners of stray pigeons). This accommodation nearby is especially handy for the fanciers because it saves them the trouble of reporting, caring for the pigeon and staying home and reduces the risk of infection in their own loft.

Wing stamps

Another way of simplifying the reporting of stray pigeons is to stamp the birds' winds. It is advisable to stamp them in several places so that if one of the impressions is spoilt, the data – name, address and telephone number or just the telephone number – can be read on another.

Name ring

The identification of stray pigeons has also been made much easier with the use of the name ring.

Extra means of identification

An extra ring or band with name, address and telephone number enables the owner to be informed immediately if a stray pigeon comes into the loft. Telephone strips (very narrow bands which can be stuck under the ring number of the permanent ring) are also being increasingly used.

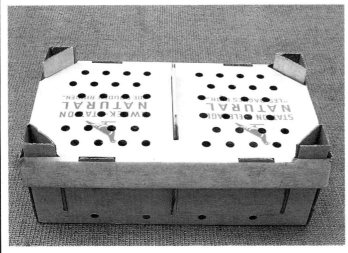

Ready to go

Boxes designed for the transport of birds are available for sending racing pigeons.

Sending back

A pigeon can be sent back post-free in response to a request for its return. The charges are paid by the owner/addressee. A sturdy box of sufficient size and provided with air holes is used for the despatch. Some wood shavings, tobacco stalks or a thick newspaper are placed on the bottom. It is stated clearly on the outside that the contents are a live pigeon.

Race calculations

The purpose of a race is not only to produce a sporting performance: it is usually also intended to yield a winner and a loser. There are few other sports where prizes lower than first are received with such acclamation, and where other positions than first are not dismissed with such remarks as 'the also-rans' or 'the places down the line'. Two methods of calculating the prizes are discussed below. Today, a team of people carrying out the calculations is often replaced by a computer.

Own speed

This is the system most used and, in theory, the most honest. The distances flown are divided by the flying time to give the average flying speed.

An example: flight distance 124.605 km = 124,605 metres time needed 1 hour 50 minutes 30 seconds = 110.5 minutes distance: time 124,605: 110.5 metres per minute = 1,127.647 metres per minute.

Speed in metres/min. →

km.	700	800	900	1000	1100	1200	1300	1400	1500	1600	1700	1800	1900
50	1.12	1.03	0.55	0.50	0.45	0.42	0.38	0.36	0.33	0.31	0.30	0.28	0.26
75	1.47	1.34	1.24	1.15	1.08	1.03	0.58	0.54	0.50	0.47	0.44	0.42	0.40
100	2.23	2.05	1.51	1.40	1.31	1.24	1.17	1.12	1.07	1.03	1.00	0.55	0.52
125	2.59	2.36	2.19	2.05	1.54	1.44	1.36	1.29	1.24	1.18	1.15	1.09	1.06
150	3.34	3.08	2.48	2.30	2.16	2.05	1.55	1.47	1.40	1.34	1.28	1.24	1.19
175	4.10	3.39	3.15	2.55	2.39	2.26	2.14	2.05	1.57	1.50	1.43	1.37	1.31
200	4.46	4.10	3.42	3.20	3.02	2.48	2.34	2.23	2.14	2.05	2.00	1.51	1.44
225	5.21	4.41	4.10	3.45	3.25	3.08	2.54	2.42	2.30	2.21	2.12	2.05	1.59
250	5.57	5.12	4.38	4.10	3.47	3.28	3.12	2.59	2.47	2.36	2.30	2.19	2.12
275	6.33	5.44	5.06	4.35	4.10	3.49	3.32	3.16	3.03	2.52	2.42	2.33	2.25
300	7.08	6.16	5.35	5.00	4.32	4.10	3.51	3.34	3.20	3.08	2.56	2.47	2.38
325	7.44	6.46	6.01	5.25	4.55	4.30	4.10	3.52	3.37	3.23	3.11	3.00	2.51
350	8.20	7.18	6.29	5.50	5.18	4.52	4.29	4.10	3.53	3.39	3.26	3.15	3.03
375	8.56	7.49	6.57	6.15	5.41	5.12	4.48	4.28	4.10	3.55	3.41	3.28	3.17
400	9.32	8.20	7.24	6.40	6.04	5.36	5.08	4.46	4.28	4.10	4.00	3.42	3.28
450	10.43	9.22	8.26	7.30	6.49	6.15	5.46	5.24	5.00	4.41	4.25	4.10	3.57
500	11.54	10.25	9.16	8.20	7.34	6.56	6.24	5.57	5.34	5.12	5.00	4.38	4.24
550	13.06	11.28	10.11	9.10	8.20	7.38	7.04	6.33	6.06	5.44	5.24	5.06	4.50
600	14.16	12.24	11.10	10.00	9.04	8.20	7.42	7.08	6.40	6.15	5.53	5.34	5.16
650	15.28	13.32	12.02	10.50	9.50	9.00	8.20	7.44	7.14	6.46	6.22	6.01	5.42
700	16.40	14.35	12.58	11.40	10.36	9.44	8.58	8.20	7.46	7.18	6.52	6.30	6.08
750	17.53	15.38	13.54	12.30	11.22	10.25	9.37	8.56	8.20	7.49	7.22	6.57	6.34
800	19.04	16.40	14.48	13.20	12.08	11.12	10.16	9.32	8.56	8.20	8.00	7.24	6.56
850	20.14	17.44	15.44	14.10	12.52	11.48	10.54	10.07	9.26	8.52	8.20	7.52	7.27
900	21.26	18.45	16.40	15.00	13.38	12.30	11.32	10.42	10.00	9.22	8.50	8.20	7.54
950	22.38	19.48	17.36	15.50	14.24	13.12	12.10	11.19	10.34	9.54	9.18	8.48	8.20
1000	23.48	20.50	18.32	16.40	15.00	13.52	12.48	11.54	11.07	10.25	10.00	9.16	8.48

Coordinates

In calculating the race data use is made of coordinates. These are two imaginary lines running in an east–west and north–south direction behind the liberation point, forming the x and y lines or axes respectively. In order to give each fancier the same chance of gaining a prize, exact measurements are carried out, to within ten metres, between the liberation point and the loft. For this, topographic maps at a scale of 1:10,000 are needed, on which a pinprick indicates the site of the loft. Data is also available for the distances to each loft measured in the field, both in new residential areas and in the countryside. Each new loft is calculated and recorded with the aid of accurate measurements. An experienced fancier usually knows by heart the distance between his loft and the liberation points he uses most.

37

NEDERL. POSTD. HOUDERS
ORGANISATIE

C O Ö R D I N A T E N
in het stelsel van het
Rijksvierkantennet

x 11588,0   y 13778,2

Duivenhok van   J. Hermans

Adres   Bannenberglaan 6
                 Waalre

Naam en nummer der vereniging
        C.C.E. 1667 – 1681

Datum van afgifte   04-03-78

Handtekening van de rekenaar

Zone system or town speed

This system is based on the assumption that all pigeons fly at about the same speed. When a competition lasts a long time, i.e. when there is a big difference between the first and the last pigeon recorded, the last pigeons appear to have flown at a considerably slower speed but this assumption is incorrect. The position in the race is determined, for example, on the basis of the speed of the first ten pigeons. If these all fly at just over 1100 metres per minute, this is the starting speed for all the participating birds. The system works well when it is applied to a limited area. It is somewhat easier to determine the result on this basis than with the own speed system and it was formerly relatively must used. A correction was applied for lofts situated close to or far from the centre.

Theoretically speaking, two lofts situated alongside each other must have the same coordinates. The point is always taken to be the flying loft, while for a fancier owning several lofts the loft with the shortest distance is taken.

QUIEVRAIN

1. Statie	6518.05	5056.85
2. ancien four à coke	6518.10	5057.60
3. pl. du petit Bruxelles	6517.00	5060.00
4. sucrerie Olivier	6520.20	5059.60
5. Chée de Brunehaut	6525.00	5057.60

ALBERT	5763.70	5495.40
ANGOULEME	3719.60	10259.20
ARCIS S/Aube	6823.30	7147.70
ARGENTON	4813.60	9264.40
ARRAS	5861.50	5189.60
ARTENAY	5147.40	7619.20
AUBERVILLERS	5546.80	6694.60
BAR LE DUC	7585.00	6876.10
BERGERAC	3931.50	11156.90
BLOIS	4710.30	8154.70
BOHAIN	6335.90	5524.40
BORDEAUX	3103.40	11123.00
BOURGES	5502.10	8727.20
BRETEUIL	5566.10	5913.70
BRETIGNY	5474.70	7046.20
BRIARE	5769.10	8119.30
BRIVES	4765.30	10886.50
CAHORS	4658.90	11640.90
CAEN	3472.80	6315.60
CAMBRAI	6197.50	5316.70
CARCASSONNE	5355.00	13036.00
CHANTILLY	5607.90	6401.00
CHARTRES	4860.10	7203.80
CHATEAUDUN	4741.80	7615.00
CHATEAUROUX	4959.70	9030.40
CHATELLERAULT	4085.00	8979.50
CHAULNES	5871.70	5718.80
CLERMONT	5583.70	6179.50
COMPIEGNE	5880.60	6146.80
CORBEIL	5601.20	7042.70
CREIL	5619.00	6315.80
CREPY en Valois	5923.00	6360.90
DAMMARTIN	5779.60	6577.80
DAX	2635.00	12340.00
DORMANS	6469.80	6537.30
DOURDAN	5255.20	7119.00
DUN	7588.00	6213.00
EPERNAY (Ville)	6699.40	6576.00
EPERNAY (Station)	6693.80	6565.60
ESTERNAY	6406.50	6926.10
ETAMPES	5364.60	7228.80
FONTAINEBLEAU	5784.00	7266.40
ISSOUDUN	5185.70	8880.80
LA FERTE S/Joua.	6086.70	6676.60
LA MOTTE-Beuvron	5234.90	8166.50
LANDRECIES	6507.40	5373.00
LAON	6458.30	5991.00
LA SOUTERRAINE	4779.30	9654.70
LIBOURNE	3360.90	11058.00
LIMOGES	4590.60	10096.90

MEAUX	5904.60	6667.70
MELUN	5735.90	7140.20
MEZIERES	7257.00	5771.70
MONTELIMAR	7299.90	11564.20
MONTLUCON	5636.80	9574.30
MORCENX	2763.00	12005.50
MONTAUBAN	4569.70	12124.20
MONTARGIS	5786.00	7718.40
NEMOURS	5749.50	7426.40
NEVERS	6072.70	8857.10
NOGENT S/Seine	6354.40	7182.20
NOYON	6018.00	5978.00
ORLEANS (Station)	5159.60	7803.80
ORLEANS	5157.80	7808.70
ORMOY VILLERS	5885.10	6394.10
PARIS (Place Concorde)	5496.70	6757.00
PAU	3148.40	12864.40
PERIGUEUX	4119.60	10799.30
POITIERS	3905.00	9236.60
Pt. Ste-MAXENCE	5714.60	6269.50
RENNES	2459.70	7485.00
RETHEL	7002.10	6066.00
RIBECOURT	5958.10	6054.60
RUFFEC	3762.50	9840.00
ROYAN	2799.60	10231.80
St-DIZIER	7424.30	7023.20
St.-DENIS	5518.50	6683.70
St-QUENTIN	6225.30	5690.40
» (Gare Allemande)	6234.80	5686.40
St-VINCENT	2417.10	12397.70
SAI BRIS	5249.00	8357.00
SEIS	6181.10	7512.20
SOISSONS	6254.70	6211.40
TOURS	4227.40	8353.20
TOURY	5197.00	7495.00
TULLE	4950.10	10754.80
VANNES	1690.50	7792.90
VENDOME	4525.00	7907.00
VERTUS	6736.00	6738.20
VERVINS	6656.00	5705.60
VIERZON	5249.00	8572.00
VICHY	6275.90	9819.40

VLIEGVELDEN :

BEAUVAIS-TILLE	5359.90	6099.00
CORMEILLES en VEXIN	5302.90	6496.70
ETAMPES-MONDESIR	5302.00	7296.80
CHARTRES-CHAMPHOL	4885.90	7185.90
ORLEANS-BRICY	5065.80	7723.20
TOURS St-Symphorien	4250.60	8300.80
CHATEAUROUX La Martinerie	5012.30	9014.90
LIMOGES-FEYTIAT	4602.70	10125.70
COGNAC (Châteaubernard)	3344.20	10225.40
BORDEAUX-MERIGNAC	2979.60	11124.90
PEA-PONT-LONG	3109.30	12776.50
BARCELONE-MUNTADOS	5080.00	15155.00
BOURGES	5486.20	8760.00

Calculation

The actual calculation is a question of mathematics, which may not interest everyone but is included for the sake of completeness. The starting point is Pythagoras' theorem:
a-squared + b-squared = c-squared,
or c = the square root of a-squared + b-squared.
a is the difference between the x coordinate of the release point and that of the loft, i.e. xR − xL = a.
b is the difference between the y coordinate of the release point and that of the loft.

The squares of a and b are summed and the square root is calculated of the result.

This gives the correct distance to the loft.

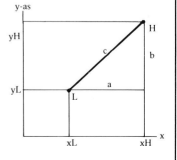

Forms of competition

In order to be able to compare the performances the pigeons produce with us and for us, all kinds of competitions are available. They exist at all levels and are adapted to the different specialisms. They also differ from country to country. We must obviously limit ourselves in the following to a summary.

Dutch races

In the Netherlands there are competitions in the sprint, middle-distance, long-distance, young birds, old birds and end-of-season categories. Often a distinction is made between 'nominated' and 'not nominated'. Nominated means depending on the position on the stake form. 'Three nominated', for example, means that it is the first three pigeons entered on the form which count. 'Four not nominated' means the four fastest birds clocked in, regardless of position on the stake form.

To enable members to assess to some extent the standard in their own club, it is possible for them to compare themselves with other clubs. This is done in joint competitions at the section and provincial levels. There are also the national competitions in which birds are entered for the national racing championship, to which special points systems apply. The latter take into account as many factors as possible to permit a comparison to be made. They include choice from a number of national races and having only a limited number of birds with which to gain points. The competition is very popular. There is something to suit everyone: individual titles in all possible sections, as well as 'the best loft in the Netherlands'.

Belgian races

The Belgian Pigeon Fanciers League organises championships in the sprint, middle-distance and long-distance categories. Each category produces its own champion, as well as the general champions. The league also arranges special competitions for young birds and for 'beginners' – people in this instance who have been practising the sport for under three years. Mention should further be made in all three main categories of the competition for the champion pigeon title and the subsidised races at the provincial level.

Diploma

This is the tangible proof and permanent memento of a performance. Many people display the diploma with appropriate pride. Cups and other trophies also keep alive the memory of crack pigeons who landed on our platforms and won a first or top prize.

About the sport

This handbook has so far been concerned with the fancier–pigeon relationship. The last few pages have been reserved for a number of aspects which are part of the hobby; they are interesting, but also important to know about.

The first steps

Anyone wishing to make a start with the keeping of racing pigeons need in principle only make a telephone call to the often colourfully named local pigeon fanciers' organization. A committee member, or even an ordinary member, will be only too pleased to provide you with the necessary information about the joys and privileges of membership of his club or association, or, if you have already decided to join, set the formalities in motion for you.

If there is no pigeon fancier among your friends or family circle, you may find the name of the secretary or the address of the club room in the telephone directory, or you may get help from the official local guide, or obtain the address or telephone number from the local council.

League addresses

If none of this helps, because the place where you live does not have a fanciers' club, you should call on the services of the national league. In Belgium this is the KBDB, the Royal Belgian Pigeon Fanciers League, Livornostraat 39, 1050 Brussels. Dutch enthusiasts can call on the services of the NPO, Dutch Racing Pigeon Owners Organisation, Landjuweel 38, 3905 PH Veenendaal.

Entry requirements

In Belgium the unsuspecting citizen who wishes to join the ranks of pigeon fanciers is unexpectedly faced with regulations laid down by the Ministries of Finance and Defence. A selection of the regulations is given here, not in order to make it seem difficult to get started, but purely for completeness' sake. The club knows all about the regulations and will generally be able to sort everything out for you.

As far as the Netherlands is concerned, the rules for training, where this might cause a nuisance, are laid down in the local police regulations, which also contain guidance on protecting farm crops. Any restrictions on flying out may also form the subject of provincial regulations.

Someone taking his first steps in the sport of pigeon racing will not have the immediate prospect of a table full of cups, nor will he give it a thought. But he will certainly feel the longing in due course to possess some of these tangible proofs of success.

Protection and restriction

The Belgian Act of 1924 for the protection of military pigeons and to restrict the use of pigeons for spying (amended by Royal Decree of 5 March 1971) is still in force and is really a tribute to the racing pigeon. Its position is evidently so important that not just anyone is allowed to keep one. Read just some of the more striking sections, to which, as the Act says, the club will help you conform.

A summary of the most interesting sections of the Belgian regulations governing admissions to the ranks of racing pigeon owners.

Section 1 – Anyone wishing to erect or maintain a loft for racing pigeons, or to keep racing pigeons, must obtain authority to do so from the mayor of his municipality. This authority may be granted only to members of a pigeon association affiliated to the National Pigeon Fanciers League, approved by the Minister of Defence.

Section 2 – . . . The mayor shall decide within 30 days of the receipt of the application. He may refuse the authority which has been properly applied for only to a person who is forbidden to keep racing pigeons under the provisions of this Act. (Section 3 shows such a person to be, for example, anyone who has been punished for catching, killing and keeping military pigeons or who has been punished for a crime against the security of the state.)

Section 5 – Each racing pigeon must be provided with a ring of the official type issued by the approved National League.

Section 6 contains a provision about a register at the town hall in which the names of persons, addresses and pigeons must be entered. A duplicate of this register is supplied by the local authority to the commandant of the cantonal brigade of the gendarmerie.

Section 7 – The military may carry out an annual census of racing pigeon lofts.

Section 9 – Any transport of racing pigeons outside the country must be accompanied by a certificate issued by the approved National League showing that the pigeons have been properly ringed and that their owners have satisfied the provisions of this Act.

Section 11 – Anyone who maliciously catches, kills or keeps a military pigeon commits an offence which is punishable with a period of imprisonment of from 8 days to 5 years . . .

Section 12 provides for the confiscation of pigeons which do not belong to our lofts. Section 13 states that legal searches for this purpose may be carried out from one hour before sunrise.

Section 14 – In wartime, the Minister of Defence may make such orders in relation to the subject of this Act as he thinks necessary for the defence of the country.

Financial regulations

Now that we are dealing with the legal framework, let's look at the Royal Decree of 6 July 1927, which is still in force. Apart from laying down regulations to ensure adherence to the previously cited Act, it contains provisions relating to the tax on the sport and on the gains from sums staked on pigeon races.

The Decree deals mainly with the rights and obligations of the National Pigeon Fanciers League. Section 4(1) states, for example, that the League must submit proposals to the Minister of Finance before 1 November of each year relating to the selling price of pigeon rings during the following year. 'The Minister of Finance shall determine the selling price, taking into account the costs of manufacture and distribution of the rings and owners' certificates, on the one hand, and the cost of issuing pigeon export certificates, on the other. The rings must be delivered within fifteen days of application.'

For our everyday practice Section 6 is of interest. 'Each racing pigeon owner must keep a regularly updated list indicating: (i) the numbers and the year of issue of the rings bought, the date of commencement of use of each ring and the description of the pigeons carrying the rings. The description must be entered within two months of the birth of the pigeons; (ii) the numbers and the year of issue of the rings attached to the pigeons kept by him, irrespective of whether he has obtained them free or paid for them, the name of the previous owner, the date at which the new owner obtained them and their description; (iii) for each pigeon, the date of transfer and the name of the new owner. This list must be retained for five years. The owners of the pigeons must submit the certificates of ownership held by them as proof that the entries are correct.'

Administration evidently covers more than just the development of our sport! Incidentally, every fancier in the Netherlands also has to submit a 'loft list' before the beginning of the race season.

'... if only mine were as good.'

The sport in tandem

Pigeon racing is an individual sport, but in recent years there has been a trend towards practising the sport in tandem with others. There have always been combinations of fanciers, some of whom are well-known in the sport, but these were generally allied lofts with each fancier retaining full responsibility for the well-being of his birds. The aim of the combination was the sport itself and was and is reflected in the results.

The current development is based much more on a shared responsibility for everything concerning the pigeons: accommodation, managing, breeding, racing. It may be the result of limited financial means or of lack of space, but such collaboration is often in any event a very good way of sharing the daily chore of caring for the pigeons, summer and winter, holiday or no holiday.

Young plus old is another excellent way of practising the sport in combination or in tandem, combining experience with youthful energy and enthusiasm. There is increasing agreement that practising the sport in tandem is an excellent solution for many people. This is particularly true of those who, because of work or leisure circumstances, do not have a lot of time at their disposal, or who live in cramped conditions.

Starting capital

The sport of pigeon racing also costs money. There is little sense in comparing expenditure in all hobbies or branches of sport as a means of making a ranking from cheap to dear. If chess, for example, is cheaper than pigeon racing and sailing much dearer, this observation has little meaning for people who only want to keep pigeons. Moreover, one is often comparing chalk with cheese: two hours of active sport a week plus training as against daily activity and daily recurring enjoyment. Lastly, a true comparison is possible only when one has a proper understanding of all the elements of every sport or hobby and that would require months of study.

It is more important, therefore, to indicate what the financial implications might be for a beginner. This produces at the same time a useful shopping list. The figures given are averages. People who are good with their hands or can call on skilled help will obviously be able to save on some items.

Housing

A neat loft about 3 metres in length and 1.8 metres deep provides ample scope for a proper start in pigeon racing. One half of the accommodation can be used for housing six pairs of old pigeons and the other half for about 15 young birds. The construction costs of such a loft vary, according to the materials and amount of do-it-yourself work, from about 1800 to 3000 guilders (£430 to £715). Buying an existing loft or using second-hand materials can produce a considerable saving. And . . . a good, cosy loft does not necessarily mean an expensive one!

Feeding

You must allow an average of 30 grammes of food per pigeon per day. In our calculation we assume an average occupancy as described above, namely 12 old and 15 young pigeons, or, on an annual basis, about 20 birds. (The annual basis is calculated as follows: an occupancy of 12 birds at the beginning and end of the year and of 27 pigeons during the summer.) We are speaking, therefore, of 20 (pigeons) × 365 (days) × 35 (grammes of food) = 255,500 grammes per annum. In 1985 the cost of a kilo of standard mixture was about 1 guilder 15 cents (27p). The annual sum spent on food therefore is about 300 guilders (£70). A further sum of about 50 guilders (£12) must be allowed for grit, minerals etc.

Veterinary care

The costs under this heading can be very low. Certainly if we have a limited number of pigeons and observe the necessary rules of hygiene, we shall have few problems and little expense in fighting disease. We should allow about 60 guilders (£14) per visit for two visits a year by the vet and inoculations against paramixo virus and pigeon pox/diphtheria.

Like every hobby and sport, keeping racing pigeons will require some investment.

Races

In order to be able to participate in races we must in the first place own a pigeon clock. The price of a new clock ranges from 600 to 1000 guilders (£140 to £240). A good second-hand clock – which will often be good for another ten years – can be bought for between 200 and 300 guilders (£50 and £70). Lastly, this indispensable instrument can be hired or borrowed. The maximum hiring cost would be 35 guilders (£8) per annum.

Transport costs also vary widely. The following rates applied in 1985:
– line-of-flight training up to 50 km: 20 cents (5p) per pigeon
– speed races up to 200 km: 40 cents (10p) per pigeon
– middle-distance races up to 500 km: 60 cents (14p) per pigeon
– long-distance races up to 1000 km: 125 cents (30p) per pigeon.

The fancier paid 25 cents (6p) per pigeon for club expenses and the costs of calculating the result and, lastly, 25 guilders (£6) for publication of the results. For the latter sum he receives weekly at home, from 1 April to 1 October, the results of all the races organised by the CCE.

Thus, if a fancier races with an average of five pigeons each Sunday for six months, or 130 pigeons in all, and he does so in the proportion 3 × speed, 2 × middle-distance and 1 × long-distance, this will cost him 127.90 guilders (£30) per annum, plus 18 guilders (= 90 × 20 cents) (£4) for participation in line-of-flight training. The rates in the CCE for members under 18 are even lower. The subscription is 50 guilders (£12) per annum and the 15 rings cost a further 25 guilders (£6).

Total

All this means that, on an annual basis, the average fancier with 12 old and 15 young pigeons does not have to lay out more than 675 guilders (£160) for the essential costs of pigeon racing. This is exclusive of accommodation costs. Extras would include the cost of a magazine subscription (40 to 50 guilders – £9.50 to £12 – per annum) and of refreshments when putting the birds in the hampers and handing in the clock.

Belgian freight and loading costs are 50 to 100 per cent higher than those in the Netherlands.

It sometimes happens that a young or very young fancier outstrips his older colleagues and wins first prize with a pigeon from a loft built to his own scale. It is not necessary – and this does not apply only to young fanciers – to have a palace at one's disposal. Small cosy lofts may also compete.

The older fancier

Pigeon racing is a sport for every age group, except that its non-energetic character partly determines the age group within which most fanciers are to be found. A survey carried out by the Belgian Van Clé Foundation ('The Sport of Pigeon Racing in Belgium, Today and Tomorrow', 1982) showed that the over-40s are the most strongly represented, followed by the 0–30 age group. Retired people (including those who have taken early retirement) make up no less than 29 per cent of pigeon fanciers. According to the same survey, pigeon racing is the fifth most popular form of leisure activity among this group – higher, for example, than angling, cycling and watching television.

Here is a Dutch voice speaking from experience (Gerard Verbart from 's-Heerenhoek): 'I am a rich man in comparison with my contemporaries. I have my pigeons. Others grow old in spirit, but a retired pigeon fancier does not. He finds daily distraction in looking after his birds. He doesn't become lonely. He has visitors and has to visit his colleagues. He plans for years ahead and is daily concerned with the future instead of the past. He is still competing. In this field there are no differences between young and old. Age doesn't count. There is a lot of misunderstanding about pigeon racing. I used to find that at work, but the outside world does not realise that the sport of pigeon racing opens up tremendous perspectives at a time when work ceases to be the main activity.'

The young fancier

Among young people the hobby is often passed on from father to son and, more rarely, from father to daughter. The two generations may form a tandem or a combination, or the young person may practise the sport with another, experienced fancier. In any event supervision, perhaps through the club, is greatly to be recommended. This is not to say that some young fanciers do not themselves already turn in outstanding performances.

At various places in the Netherlands there are separate youth sections with their own competitions and a modified stake system. Much attention is also paid to the youth category at the national show and in the national 'Who can beat them?' competition.

School lofts

In Belgium, in particular, some schools have established pigeon lofts as a result of the efforts of the national propaganda committee of the KBDB (Royal Belgian Pigeon Fanciers League). These obviously stand or fall with the enthusiasm of one of the teachers. Apart from being a source of inspiration for contact between human being and bird, the pigeons also provide welcome teaching material. One has only to think of the mathematics of the co-ordinate system, not to mention the potential for history and geography lessons etc.

National shows

The Dutch national league holds a show every year. The show includes the national exhibition, a youth day, the handing over of the prizes for the Dutch championship and for the national competitions. Much attention is paid to international contacts, particularly with fellow Belgian fanciers, during the show. Belgium has a federal day which is held in a different province each year.

Visitors, not just from the Netherlands, are warmly welcomed.

A break from the throngs of visitors passing the exhibition cages.

Sales

We have already seen that beginners obtain by far the greater proportion of their pigeons free or in exchange from an old hand. It is certainly not recommended that the purchaser who is starting out should over-look lofts in his neighbourhood with a good record on the principle that it is better to go further afield. He will often obtain, in addition, someone who will give free advice and take an interest in his birds.

It is noticeable how low prices sometimes seem to frighten people off rather than act as an attraction. Besides this way of acquiring birds and purchase in the market, there are the public sales from reputable lofts which are noted for their good material. The sales may be of late or early young, partial sales or total sales. We are somewhat hesitant about partial sales, because the likelihood of acquiring pigeons of a proven quality is very low.

The disadvantage of total sales is that a lot of money often has to be paid for really good specimens. On the other hand, one does know what one is getting for one's money. Total sales following the death of a champion fancier, for instance, always command great interest.

'Natural' feeding

Attention was paid on p. 105 to feeding pigeons with grain germs, seeds and pulses. At the end of 1984 the Probio Foundation published, for fanciers who are interested in 'natural' management, a daily diet sheet for widowers and, in rather smaller quantities, for their hens and young birds.

Day	Food	Drinking water	Supplement
Saturday (day of return home)	– purging mixture or barley – maize – good quantity of wheat germs peas	– sage, thyme and stinging nettle tea	– varied mixture of grit, shells, lime, stone etc. – some poultry minerals or other mineral mixture, if desired
Sunday	– see Saturday menu	– see Saturday menu	– see Saturday menu
Monday	– 1 tbsp mixed grain feed per pigeon: 1/2 purging & 1/2 race mixture. With onset of mid. & long-dist. races switch to ordinary race mixture, depending on effort required	– plantain and dandelion tea and a little miso in water every three weeks	– In addition to the menu of the last 2 days lighly moisten the grain with lemon juice or, for long dist., sunflower oil, mixed with 1 tbsp seaweed & pure beer yeast per kg food
Tuesday	– see Monday menu	– pure water	– see Saturday menu; a little spinach, lettuce & dandelion leaf, if des.
Wednesday	– tbsp race mixture – pinch fine seed (per pigeon)	– pure water	– see Monday menu
Thursday	– light feed in the morning; in the evening a full trough of race mixture (remove leftovers after 1/2 hour) – a little fine seed per pigeon	– pure water	– see Saturday menu
Friday	– with onset of mid- & long-dist races full trough in afternoon & small amount peanuts & fine seeds; – for speed races full meal in morning & some pea or maize germs in afternoon	– pure water	– see Saturday menu

International organisation

The national racing pigeon organisations are combined under the aegis of the FCI, the Fédération Colombophile Internationale. The activities of this worldwide organisation, with affiliated national leagues from Australia to the United States and from Japan to Trinidad, are co-ordinated from Brussels (Livornostraat 39). After the last meeting of the affiliated countries in Oporto (1985), the total membership was 36 countries, which is not to say that the sport is limited to these countries.

The FCI organises the International Racing Pigeon Olympiade, which has already been referred to in these pages. Every two years the best fliers and the handsomest specimens from the participating countries are shown at the Olympiade, which is held in one of the member countries. Although participation in such an event is restricted, which means that there are also other champion pigeons, such a show is nevertheless of great significance. An international exchange of information of this kind can also improve the standard of the sport. Nor should we underestimate the value of participants from all over the world meeting at such a gathering.

The Olympiade is also the occasion for the general meeting of members of the FCI. In addition, the executive of the Federation meets once or twice during the year.

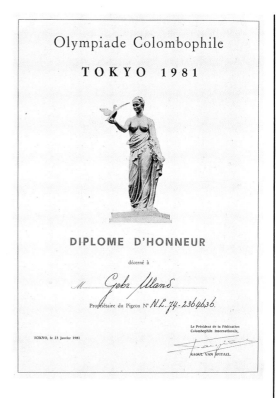

Sport across the frontiers

The sport in other countries naturally does not differ greatly from that in Belgium and the Netherlands, although it is noticeable that the widowhood system is practised rather less outside Western Europe.

Moreover, climatic and geographical differences have some influence. In very hot countries, for example, one finds almost exclusively open lofts, enclosed by wire netting. In very cold countries, on the other hand, the lofts are well insulated and fitted with very little glass. Fanciers and pigeons in mountainous countries, such as Switzerland, are very restricted because of the mountain barriers, while in countries with few natural obstacles longer flights are possible.

The sport of pigeon racing, which has an estimated total of some 700,000 'official' fanciers, is expanding greatly in such countries as Taiwan and Malta.

*The view from both sides
of the table at the most
recent Olympiade, at
Oporto in Portugal 1985*

A flutter

In all parts of the world where pigeons are raced people like to 'have a flutter'. In Taiwan, for example, where only young birds are raced, enormous sums of money are sometimes involved. In Denmark (photograph), this aspect of pigeon racing has similarities with the betting on horse races as practised in the Low Countries. Bets are placed, for example, on 20 pigeons from a particular region. The birds are exhibited and the punters are able to place their bets at the windows. The results are immediately ranked by computer, so that the punters know quite quickly after the race whether they have won anything.

Organisation in the Netherlands

In 1985 there were approximately 56,000 active racing pigeon fanciers in the Netherlands and they belonged to some 1,400 clubs. The co-ordinating body since 1980 has been the Dutch Racing Pigeon Owners Organisation (NPO); until 1980 there were seven different leagues in the Netherlands which were federated in the NPO. The NPO possessed too little power, however, from the legal point of view and the real power was in the hands of the various leagues.

After years of preparation and discussion and a number of failed attempts, a real merger was achieved in 1980. The Olympiade which was organised in the Netherlands in 1979 and enjoyed tremendous interest, must certainly have played an important psychological part.

An important element in the unification process was the standpoint taken by the Dutch League of Saturday Racers. As may be inferred from the name, the membership of this league consisted of fanciers who raced only on Saturdays. But it would be more accurate to say that they did not wish to race on Sundays. This was mainly for reasons of principle: their religion did not allow them to practise sport or any other hobby on the 'Lord's Day'. These fanciers were to be found mainly in the west, north and east of the Netherlands, and it is now a constantly shrinking group. As already mentioned on page 62, the Netherlands has a special association devoted to exhibiting and to the training of judges. This 'First Dutch Group of Judges' was founded as early as 1925. The objective is to instruct the Dutch fancier about what is an acceptable pigeon, physic, rather than purely in relation to racing achievements.

The Netherland has about 70 recognised central lofts which are listed in the ring book. The latter contains much other interesting information about the practice of the sport.

The official publication of the NPO and its sections is the *Neerlands Postduiven Orgaan (Dutch Racing Pigeon Journal)*.

Structure of the organisation

The highest organ of the NPO, with a deciding voice in policy matters, is the general meeting. The latter is attended by delegates of the organisation's 30 sections, who are chosen by proportional representation (the larger the section, the larger the number of delegates). The NPO executive has nine members. Within the organisation there are various committees, such as the clocks committee, the disciplinary committee, the arbitration committee, the transport committee, the national show committee and the youth committee.

Each section is free to arrange its own race programme and this applies in principle to all the clubs belonging to that section.

Organisation in Belgium

At the beginning of 1985 there were some 1,800 clubs or associations in Belgium actively engaged in our sport. Their committee members do a tremendous amount of work on a voluntary basis so that their over 98,000 registered fanciers can race their birds. The clubs have a national co-ordinating body in the KBDB, the Royal Belgian Pigeon Fanciers League, with its headquarters in the Livornostraat in Brussels, which is also the editorial address of the official journal, the *Bondsblad* (*League Magazine*).

The institution of judges is unknown in Belgium, as are large-scale shows, except during the periof before an Olympiade. Many clubs, however, do hold what might be called 'Sunday morning shows', which are not as strictly controlled as in the Netherlands, but are excellent for social contacts. Over half a million pigeons are exhibited each year in this way in public. All over the world the sport uses pigeons of Belgian origin or their descendants, which underlines yet again the pre-eminence of Belgium in the world of racing pigeons.

Structure of the organisation

The league operates at three levels: national, provincial and regional.

The organisational structure of the league is shown in the diagram below:

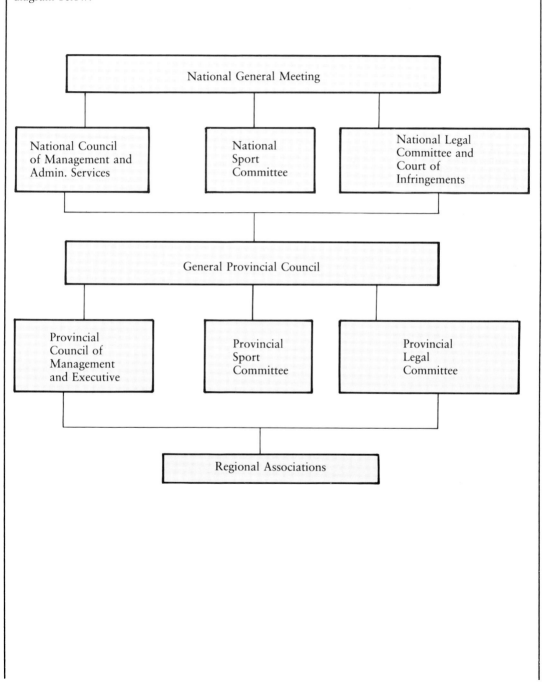

Index